# A Heritage Restored

BOOKS BY ROBERT MURPHY

*The Haunted Journey*
*The Peregrine Falcon*
*The Pond*
*The Golden Eagle*
*Wild Geese Calling*
*The Phantom Setter and Other Stories*
*A Certain Island*
*Wild Sanctuaries*
*The Mountain Lion*
*A Heritage Restored*

ROBERT MURPHY

# A Heritage Restored

## America's Wildlife Refuges

FOREWORD BY STEWART L. UDALL

E. P. Dutton Co., Inc.    New York

# Acknowledgments

It would be impossible to acknowledge individually
the help of all those whose aid and counsel have gone
into the writing of this book. Many of them
are naturalists or researchers living or dead whose
accumulation of knowledge of the natural world has
been invaluable. Equally invaluable has been
the cooperation of the people on the Bureau of Sport
Fisheries and Wildlife who advised me or
took me about. I am greatly in their debt, and wish
to express my heartfelt appreciation.

*First Edition*

*Copyright © 1969 by Robert Murphy*
*All rights reserved. Printed in the U.S.A.*

*Published simultaneously in Canada by*
*Clarke, Irwin & Company Limited, Toronto and Vancouver*

*Library of Congress Catalog Card Number: 76-83969*

*Maps drawn by George Buctel*

*Designed by The Etheredges*

*C59790/91*

# Contents

*Foreword* BY STEWART L. UDALL     7

PART ONE
NATIONAL WILDLIFE REFUGES
AND CONSERVATION

*Introduction*     11

*Chapter One     What Happened to Our Animals*     17

*Chapter Two     What Happened to Our Birds*     23

*Chapter Three     Bird Migration and Its Importance
in Conservation*     27

PART TWO

THE REFUGES

Region One    The Northwest    37
Malheur    39
The Klamath Basin    43
Bison Range    47
Hawaiian Islands    52
The Alaskan Refuges    57
KENAI    58
KODIAK    62
NUNIVAK    69

Region Two    The Southwest    75
Aransas    76
Wichita Mountains    82

Region Three    The Midcontinent and Pothole Country    89
Agassiz    91
J. Clark Salyer    94
Lostwood    99

Region Four    The Southeast    101
Cape Romain    102
Okefenokee    106

Region Five    The Northeast    111
Moosehorn    113

Epilogue    119

Appendix: The National Wildlife Refuges in Brief    120

Illustration Credits    126

Index    127

Many of us Americans think of National Wildlife Refuges as rigidly defined sanctuaries for wildlife. They are, of course, much more than this: imaginative management has found ways in which they serve elemental needs of both wildlife and man—because man and wildlife must live together, as probably twenty million people are currently learning each year on the refuges.

Perhaps we think of these areas in rigid definitions because the burgeoning human population of the United States is forcing too many of us to live in squares enclosing still smaller squares, closed and stacked . . . an existence within a rigid geometry that stifles free spirits, beast or human.

*We* need sanctuaries just as the animals need refuges. The graphic arts of every world culture are embellished with allusions to or representations of animals and plants. Art, literature, and the common references of conservation remind us, within our urban enclosures, of the wider ranges and freer creatures, thus stimulating our latent urge to replenish our souls by returning to our sources. In green pastures, on great sweeps of desert or in swamp solitude, wild sanctuaries restore the spirit of man and release him from rectangles.

The refuges serve different specifics while preserving their basic purpose; they vary as the climate varies across the far-flung reaches of our wide land. In my native Arizona, where much space is still in the public domain, large refuges have been created from public lands to protect rare desert species such as the desert bighorn sheep, or

for migrating waterfowl who need "wateringholes" in their arid flight, or to safeguard habitat that may be needed for a variety of species.

Here the problem may be international: to guard the Sonoran pronghorn antelope, an international area has been set up for this endangered mammal along the border. Million-acred Cabeza Prieta Game Range in Arizona bears most of these antelope existing in this country.

In these great Western refuges, there are far more acres than people over the face of the land. By contrast, consider new and comparatively tiny Great Swamp National Wildlife Refuge in New Jersey, from which you can almost see the storied towers of Manhattan. Here, at considerable expense to Federal funds and with large donations from interested citizens, many thousands of schoolchildren—and many an adult, are introduced to wild living things for the first time in their lives.

A desert in Arizona and a swamp in New Jersey are very different in climate and size, but they have a clear common objective: protecting wildlife for human pleasure.

We need the wildlife refuge and the human sanctuary in the midst of people—not *in* the metropolis, perhaps, but close to it. Consider Parker River Refuge on the Massachusetts coast, surrounded by twenty million people but offering a lonely bird walk among the sand dunes or a small cove for fishing, a resting place for waterfowl, a haven for shorebirds.

These refuges are as varied as the wildlife and the people that they serve. Some of them are tiny islands that are colonial nesting sites: vital links in the continent-spanning chain of migration for songbirds. Others are vast areas for wide-ranging game animals moving over ranges larger than some states.

So while hundreds of thousands of people are visiting such refuges as Wichita Mountains, to see the "frontier" of buffalo, longhorn cattle, Western grasses and prairie dogs, only a few will ever see the Aleutian Islands National Wildlife Refuge or the Arctic National Wildlife Range, both in Alaska. Not many people, even, will set foot upon Red Rock Lakes Refuge in Montana, the area that rescued trumpeter swans from oblivion.

But Robert Murphy has provided here some fascinating accounts of these distant areas that are so difficult to reach, along with his reports on the closer refuges. I am impressed with his knowledge of the vast tracts in Alaska. Indeed, he probably has supplied the most complete account of these refuges to be found anywhere outside government investigative reports—and *his* style is more readable.

At the risk of being repetitious, let me remind you again that our refuges are managed for wildlife but to benefit man; they are not locked up; more and more they serve those of us who are bird watchers, hunters, photographers, fishermen, students—or just seekers of seclusion.

I know there are those who believe, almost instinctively, that all refuges should be inviolate sanctuaries from which all humans are excluded. And there are other demands that refuges be developed as vacation spots, as playgrounds with facilities for popular sports and mass games. But there is no mutually exclusive mode of living, on a refuge or in the human huddle, and if we are to have a balanced existence in this nation, man and wildlife must learn to live together, not exclusively.

So our policy on the National Wildlife Refuges might be stated in its simplest terms as this: to manage the smallest island and the largest game range in the system for proper usage by living things.

As you travel America, on long tour or short, include the refuges in your itinerary. On these wildlife lands you can see ducks and geese by the tens of thousands; you can see alligators and songbirds; you might see some of the sixteen endangered species living in these areas. They provide habitat for musk-oxen and mallards, for alligators and avocets, for birds and bighorn. All these species and many, many more are a part of life—and refuges are for the living.

—*Stewart L. Udall*

# PART ONE

# National Wildlife Refuges and Conservation

*Western grebes sit low in the water and swim with their heads erect.*

*Some 20,000 Canada geese winter at Bombay Hook.*

I don't recall how many years it has been since I first heard of a place called Bombay Hook. Bombay Hook, it appeared, was a National Wildlife Refuge. I lived in Pennsylvania at the time, and it was a drive of about an hour from my house, and open to the public. There were roads through it, and at certain seasons great congregations of migratory birds—Canada and snow geese, ducks and shorebirds, herons, hawks, and other birds of the marsh, as well as songbirds— could be seen there, close at hand and living their natural lives. This sounded very interesting and unusual, so I went to Bombay Hook.

The refuge was near Dover, the capital of Delaware, on that section of the flat coastal plain which rarely rises ten feet above sea level, farming country with patches of brushy woodland. I registered at the small building across the road from headquarters, as visitors are requested to do, and took the gravel road before me. Soon I was driving along the top of a long dike that holds the first freshwater impoundment. The impoundment was to the left, and there were a great number of black ducks, mallards, pintails, and Canada geese on the water close at hand; to the right were a ditch and a great tidal marsh, golden in the afternoon sun, that extends far eastward to Delaware Bay. Red-winged blackbirds flitted among the roadside reeds; there was an occasional egret wading offshore, with a slow-flying marsh hawk or two and a pair of red-tailed hawks hunting the marsh. A bald eagle perched on a distant dead tree, and was confirmed with the binoculars.

All these creatures were aware of me but went about their business with an air of confidence, as though they knew that they were in sanctuary and that I also knew it. All the while there was a traffic of ducks, with an occasional bunch of geese in the air talking together in that mellow music of theirs that never fails to stir the blood. That great sweep of golden marsh and blue water, full of life and vitality, was the sort of place that one often wished he could get into but hadn't been able to find before.

I went on to the next impoundment, then through fields where grain was grown for the avian visitors. Deer watched me from the edge of cover, and there were many corners where great blue herons, curlews, and others gathered together or held a little space for themselves.

Toward dusk, just before I went home, I stood in a low tangle of trees and watched and listened to company after company of geese go over me in the rosy sky, set their wings, and plane down toward one of the ponds for the night. The rise and fall of their voices, and the welcoming voices of those already on the water, followed me toward the gate. It had been one of the most invigorating and satisfactory days that I had spent in a long time, and I fell into the habit of returning occasionally, at all seasons of the year. There was always something interesting to see, and it gave the feeling of a place, seemingly remote and largely untouched, but readily accessible, a piece of wild America now so largely vanished, so difficult to find, that brought a lift to the spirit.

Getting to know one refuge made me want to know more of them in a country so

Ocean

Pacific

**WASHINGTON**

FLATTERY ROCKS
QUILLAYUTE NEEDLES
COPALIS
WILLAPA
CAPE MEARES
THREE ARCH ROCKS
MATIA I.
JONES I.
SMITH I.
SAN JUAN
DUNGENESS
LITTLE PEND OREILLE
RIDGEFIELD
TOPPENISH
COLUMBIA
TURNBULL
KOOTENAI
PABLO
NINEPIPE
NATIONAL BISON
RAVALLI
CREEDMAN COULEE
L. THIBADEAU
PISHKUN
WILLOW CR.
BLACK COULEE
BENTON L.
HEWITT L.
BOWDOIN
MEDICINE L.
CHARLES M. RUSSELL
AGASSIZ

**OREGON**

★ Portland
BASKETT SLOUGH
ANKENY
WM. L.
FINLEY
KLAMATH FOREST
OREGON IS.
UPPER KLAMATH
CONBOY L.
McNARY
COLD SPRINGS
McKAY CREEK
MALHEUR
HART MOUNTAIN
LOWER KLAMATH
TULE L.
CLEAR L.
MODOC

**IDAHO**

DEER FLAT
CAMAS
RED ROCK LAKES
HAILSTONE
HALFBREED L.
GRAYS L.
MINIDOKA

WAR HORSE
L. MASON
LAMESTEER

**MONTANA**

NORTH DAKOTA
(SEE INSET)
TAMAR

**NORTH DAKOTA**

BEAR BUTTE

**SOUTH DAKOTA**

SAND L.
WAUBAY
LACREEK
FORT NIOBRARA
VALENTINE
NORTH PLATTE
CRESCENT L.
L. ANDES
DE SOTO

**WYOMING**

NATIONAL ELK
SEEDSKADEE
PATHFINDER
BAMFORTH
HUTTON L.

**NEVADA**

CHARLES SHELDON
SHELDON ANTELOPE
**1**
ANAHO I.
RUBY L.
FALLON
STILLWATER
MERCED
PAHRANGAT
DESERT GAME

**UTAH**

LOCOMOTIVE SPRINGS
BEAR R.
OURAY
BROWNS PARK
FISH SPRINGS

**COLORADO**

**2**
MONTE VISTA
ALAMOSA
MAXWELL

**CALIFORNIA**

SACRAMENTO
DELEVAN
COLUSA
SUTTER
FARALLON
PIXLEY
KERN

**NEBRASKA**

SQUAW CREEK
KIRWIN

**KANSAS**

QUIVIRA
SALT PLAINS

**NEW MEXICO**

★ Albuquerque
LAS VEGAS
BUFFALO LAKE
BOSQUE DEL APACHE
MULESHOE
BITTER L.
SAN ANDRES

**OKLAHOMA**

WASHITA
WICHITA MTS.
TISHOMINGO
HAGERMAN

**ARIZONA**

HAVASU L.
CIBOLA
SALTON SEA
KOFA
IMPERIAL
CABEZA PRIETA

**TEXAS**

**U.S.S.R.**

ARCTIC ▲

CHAMISSO

**ALASKA**

**BERING SEA**

BERING SEA
NUNIVAK
HAZEN BAY
CLARENCE RHODE
TUXEDNI
KENAI
PRIBILOF
KODIAK
IZEMBEK
SEMIDI
BOGOSLOF
SIMEONOF
ALEUTIAN IS.

**CANADA**

**MEXICO**

ST. LAZARIA
HAZY IS.
FORRESTER I.

ARANSAS
SANTA ANA
LAGUNA ATASCOSA

0    200    400
Miles

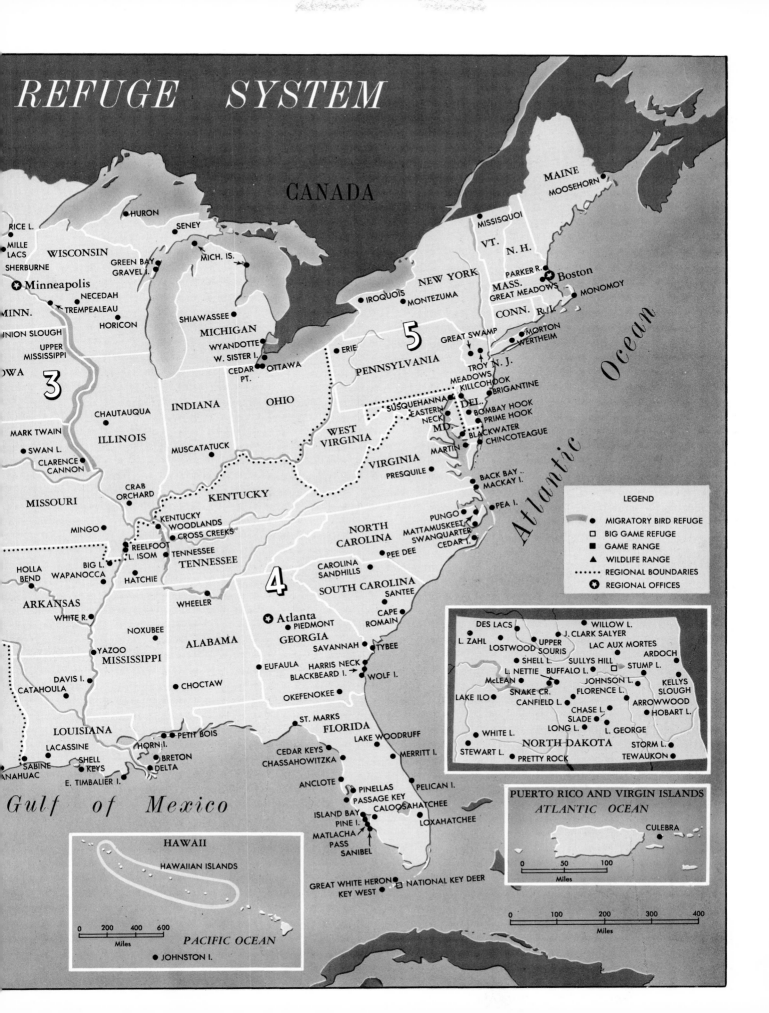

*A bird of open country, the marsh hawk builds a nest of sticks and grass stems on the ground near water.*

*No bird is more characteristic of the National Wildlife Refuge System than the Canada goose. A flying Canada is its official symbol. This large goose is easily identified by a prominent white stripe which runs under its chin from side to side.*

large and varied and beautiful as ours. I made some inquiries of the Bureau of Sport Fisheries and Wildlife in Washington, and was given a good deal of information. I found that there are over three hundred refuges, that the system was divided into five regions, and that the history of the refuges (given in more detail in the following chapters) was the history of conservation in the United States. I also saw that I wanted to go to more refuges and write a book about them. I didn't realize that this enterprise would eventually place me practically eyeball to chilly eyeball with a large Okefenokee alligator in Georgia, within fifteen yards of a very large Kodiak brown bear in Alaska, or within stone-throwing range of the very rare musk ox on Nunivak Island in the Bering Sea.

*Mallards are perhaps the best known of all North American ducks. After mating, the males leave the females and can often be seen in groups of two or three or several hundred.*

The five regions and some of the refuges in them are described in this book. The refuges I visited were chosen because they are typical of the country in which they are found or because the creatures they contained were unusual, endangered, or particularly concerned with the history of conservation. I wanted to see them all, but because of their number I couldn't do so. I wanted to see the wonderful diversity of America, and the choice was personal; looking over the list, I said to myself: I want to go there and there and there. In some cases I chose refuges so remote and difficult to get to that not many people will ever see them, but I thought that people would like to hear about them and the rare birds and animals that live upon them. However, many of those described in the following pages are within reach, and the appendix at the end of the book gives a selected list of refuges and the address of refuge headquarters. An inquiry addressed to the refuge manager at any of them will bring you a leaflet which briefly describes them and their wildlife, how to get there, and often what the nearby accommodations are, as well as the recreational possibilities aside from observation. Where no camping is allowed but there is camping nearby, this has been indicated.

The Bureau of Sport Fisheries and Wildlife of the Department of the Interior, Washington, D.C. 20240, also publishes a *Directory of National Wildlife Refuges,* as well as many other publications dealing with the subject, any of which can be had for the asking. The *Directory* listing is by states, and indicates the primary species benefited on each area. The individual refuge leaflets are informative, and in many cases there are bird lists and mammal lists as well. You can take your pick of the refuges in accordance with your inclination and your ability to get to them.

At one time there wasn't much enthusiasm within the Bureau toward the idea of actually welcoming visitors to the refuges.

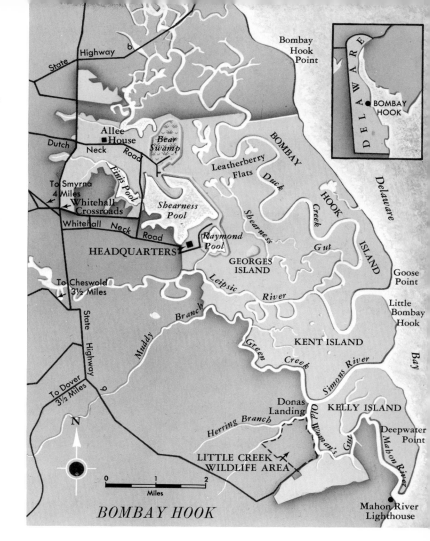

BOMBAY HOOK

They were sanctuaries where attempts were being made to bring back animals or birds that were in trouble, and people would interfere with this difficult enterprise. In many cases the enterprise has been quite successful —as, for instance, in the cases of the American bison or buffalo, the pronghorn antelope, the trumpeter swan, the Canada goose, and some of the ducks. We aren't out of the woods yet; there are still some endangered species; but we are far enough out of the woods to have changed some of the original thinking. There is no place on refuges for the hordes of people who go to the National Parks, which are administered by a different bureau and have no connection with the refuge system, but the Bureau is now very glad to welcome those who are genuinely interested in the

15

*Long-billed curlews, now rare in the eastern United States, are common at Malheur at all seasons except winter. Their bills reach a length of 8½ inches, making them the longest billed bird in the sandpiper family.*

*Both young and old can enjoy the recreational opportunities of the refuge system.*

wildlife that was so wretchedly and wastefully treated before the idea of conservation began to take hold in our country.

The first three chapters tell what happened to our wildlife and why the refuge system was necessary if much of it wasn't to vanish forever, and set forth some facts about the migrations of geese, ducks, and other birds that are necessary to know in order to understand why the refuge system is set up as it is. Descriptions of the refuges follow. I hope that the reader will want to visit and explore them and that they will give him as much outdoor pleasure as they have given me.

I should like to express here my great appreciation to the personnel of the Bureau of Sport Fisheries and Wildlife for the kindness and help I have been given, and to four men in the past, in particular: Theodore Roosevelt and Gifford Pinchot, the fathers of federal conservation in this country; Jay N. Darling, who brought the small and struggling Biological Survey to the attention of the nation and started it on its way to being the far-flung conservation enterprise it is today; and J. Clark Salyer, who probably more than any other man is responsible for the present refuge system.

—R.M.

# CHAPTER ONE

# What Happened to Our Animals?

No continent was settled and exploited so quickly as the continent of North America. What had been a primitive wilderness became the world's greatest industrial nation in less than a hundred years. As the people increased, they spread out over the face of the land and began to change it. They were very wasteful; they seemed to hate nature instead of trying to work with her. The new continent was so vast, and its resources seemingly so inexhaustible, that they didn't think of the future.

As early as 1760 they were wantonly slaughtering the game. Ring hunts, in which a number of hunters circled a big area and closed in on it, shooting everything they saw, were held. One that was held in Snyder County, Pennsylvania, in 1760, killed 41 mountain lions, 114 bobcats, 109 wolves, 112 foxes, 17 black bears and 1 albino, 111 buffalo, 3 fishers, 1 otter, 12 wolverines, 3 beavers, and 500 smaller animals; they took a few hides and the buffalo tongues, and piled the carcasses up as tall as the trees and set them afire. This senseless killing went on until 1849, wastefully exterminated many species in many localities, and wasn't confined to Pennsylvania. As the population increased, more of the killing was done by market hunters, but sportsmen were very wasteful too.

As the western country was opened up,

Beau Brummell appeared in London in a beaver hat, and the style became so popular that European beaver were practically exterminated for their fur. Beaver along the eastern seaboard of America went next, and the trappers moved west. Mountain men like Jim Bridger and others led the way, trapped out the Plains, and vanished into the Rockies. They hunted beaver down to the headwaters of the most obscure creeks, and brought out so much fur that great fur companies were formed which debauched the Indians with whiskey, gave them guns to kill each other's men, and carried on private wars.

The beavers, whose primitive numbers have been estimated to be around 60,000,000, were almost exterminated before silk hats came into fashion and ruined the market for beaver fur. The beaver hunt had taught Americans a great deal about the West and Canada, and the fur companies, searching for something to do next, began to think of the buffalo.

This great beast, whose primitive numbers were about the same as the beaver's, was fairly well distributed across the country from Cape Cod to California, south of the Great Lakes and up into Canada. They were never very plentiful in forested country and had been exterminated east of the Mississippi by 1830; they gathered in vast numbers on the

Great Plains from the Mississippi to the Rockies, from Saskatchewan to Mexico. Experienced observers estimated that one herd along the Arkansas River during the Civil War contained about 4,000,000 animals, and it was only one of a number of herds at the time.

Indians, wolves, severe winters, and prairie fires killed some of them, but it wasn't until white traders began to exchange whiskey and firearms for hides that the Indians began to kill wantonly. Railroads spread across the West, and professional hide, tongue, and meat hunters came in with them. The railroads had divided the buffalo into northern and southern herds, and the southern herd was hunted down first. Everybody ate buffalo; the railroads ran excursions for the purpose of shooting buffalo, and thousands of tons of meat were left to rot on the Plains. Killing buffalo was the main industry over a vast section of the country for years.

*In the nineteenth century, buffalo hides were processed in frontier towns before shipment eastward. This photograph of stacks of hides was taken in 1874 in Dodge City, Kansas.*

The northern herd took a little longer to exterminate, but after a railroad was put through its country the hunters descended upon it; by 1883 the herd was gone. A few were left in very wild country, but they were hunted down; and when the American Museum decided it had better get a buffalo group they couldn't find a wild buffalo, and had to buy hides from cowboys, taxidermists, and Buffalo Bill's Wild West Show. The most numerous big-game animal in America was brought down from millions to nothing in thirty years or so. Their bones whitened the prairies for hundreds of miles, and were gathered by farmers and sold for fertilizer or to refine sugar.

So many people were horrified when they learned of this slaughter that their protests led President Theodore Roosevelt to make the Wichita Mountains Forest Reserve (page 82) a game sanctuary, and in 1907 buffalo were brought in from the New York Zoo and liberated there. Two years later the National Bison Range in Montana (page 47) was established. These were our first refuges for big-game animals that we had apparently wiped out.

Another animal which existed in millions on the Plains was the pronghorn, often incorrectly called antelope. It is the only animal of its genus in the world; a buck pronghorn weighs about 100 to 125 pounds, and stands about 3 feet high at the shoulders. Pronghorns can outrun anything on the continent, except possibly a good thoroughbred horse, and have superb eyesight. They escape their enemies by seeing them at a great distance and running away, but they are very curious. A hunter who conceals himself and waves a handkerchief on a stick can attract them within range. Though they have become wary of this trick, in the early days it was fatal to them.

Ernest Thompson Seton has quoted a

*The Indians coaxed the curious pronghorn into shooting range*
*with a pole holding feathers or strips of hide,*
*as portrayed in this George Catlin painting from the 1830's.*
*White men soon adopted the trick.*

letter from a man which says in effect: "In the winter of 1868 I saw a herd of antelope in the Cache le Poudre Valley of Colorado that was ten or twelve miles long and up to 660 feet wide. That winter many wagonloads were brought into Denver and sold, 3 or 4 carcasses for 25¢." Seton estimates that there were approximately 2,000,000 pronghorns in this herd, and it was a small part of the population; pronghorns outnumbered the buffalo at the time.

By 1908 the Biological Survey, now the Bureau of Sport Fisheries and Wildlife, estimated that there were only 17,000 prong-

horns left, and many people thought this estimate too high. This was probably the low point of the pronghorn, which had to survive as best it could on the National Bison Range and in the National Parks until 1931, when the Sheldon Antelope Refuge was established to protect it. Later, the Charles Sheldon Antelope Range and the Hart Mountain Refuge were added to give it additional protection. From that time on, the pronghorn has increased and is now out of danger.

Another animal that moved in herds was the wapiti, commonly called elk; like the buffalo, it ranged over most of the United States,

19

and its primitive number probably reached 10,000,000. It is a big, handsome creature, standing about 5 feet high; some of the bulls weigh over 1,000 pounds and have spectacular antlers that sometimes measure 60 inches along the beams. They spend the summers in high country and migrate lower in the fall. Many hunters moved along with a herd and shot every elk in it, and when the West was fenced for cattle they couldn't reach their winter ranges. Besides being shot for their

antlers or their meat, many bulls were shot just for their two canine teeth, which were worn on watch fobs by members of a fraternal organization. By 1910 their number had been reduced by 80 percent, and in 1911 Congress established the National Elk Refuge to protect them in winter. Many visitors participate in the feeding of the elk there. They also have been snatched back from extinction, and can be seen in several of the states.

The sea otter was another animal that

*At the National Elk Refuge
in Jackson Hole, Wyoming,
two bull elk
engage in a sparring match.
As many as 11,000 elk
winter here.*

lived sociably in herds, and it was treated as shamefully as the rest. It wore the costliest fur in the world, and lived in great numbers in North Pacific and Alaskan waters. It was found by the Russians when they discovered Alaska, and was hunted down until it was nearly exterminated. The Aleutian Islands National Wildlife Refuge was established in 1913 to protect the few that remained, and since that time it has increased again and is now out of danger.

Some of the refuges described later were established for big-game animals that had almost vanished, and from these chapters the reader can see what has been done. In fact, most of the refuges were established to restore vanishing creatures, with the exception of the Alaska refuges, which are there to forestall the necessity of starting over again with such splendid animals as the Kenai moose, the largest in the world, and the big brown, or Kodiak, bear.

*Unlike the white pelican of inland waters, the brown pelican
is a sea-loving bird, nesting and raising its young
on coastal islands and sandbars.*

# CHAPTER TWO

# What Happened to Our Birds?

A number of our birds, whose primitive populations ran into the billions, fared badly too. The passenger pigeon was probably the most numerous; it may have been the most numerous bird in the world. Larger and more colorful than the mourning dove, it moved about in flocks that darkened the sun for days at a time, and Audubon saw one flock that he estimated held 1,115,136,000 birds; many flocks like this flowed like vast rivers across the sky from the Atlantic to the Rockies, from Hudson Bay to Mexico. It seems incredible that a bird so numerous could be killed off, but the last one died in the Cincinnati Zoo in 1914.

The Carolina parakeet, our only native parrot, was a naïve, pretty, brilliantly colored bird that lived in great flocks in the valleys of the Mississippi and Ohio rivers and in southern swamps. Its plumage was so much in demand for women's hats that it was shot out, and nobody has seen one since 1904. Eskimo curlews moved south along the Atlantic Coast in the fall and through the Great Plains in the spring in vast flocks, and were shot at mating time by the wagonload; there may be a few of them left, but if they are not already extinct they soon will be. Many shorebirds, like the plovers, yellowlegs, godwits, curlews, avocets, rails, and snipe, were shot by the hundreds of thousands in spring and fall; hosts of them nested along the Atlantic

Coast, and their eggs were collected for food. Great Egg Harbor and Little Egg Inlet in New Jersey were so named because they were famous egg-collecting grounds. These birds were drastically reduced, but laws prohibiting the shooting of them came in time to save them from extinction. Whooping and sandhill cranes were shot at every opportunity, and the spread of farms across the country wiped out their ancient nesting grounds. Protection has brought back sandhills, but the fate of the whoopers is still in doubt. They are discussed in the chapter on Aransas (page 76), where they winter. The trumpeter swan, the largest of our waterfowl, nearly became extinct, but protection has at last brought it out of danger. The ivory-billed woodpecker will probably disappear because its habitat has been destroyed by the march of civilization, and the California condor, our largest vulture, is in the same plight.

There are a number of creatures which were not wantonly overshot for sport or the market, but their continued existence is doubtful because their requirements are too specialized in a country that is changing as rapidly as ours. The beautiful little Everglades kite feeds only upon a certain species of snail, which is disappearing because the marshes in which it lives are being drained; Kirtland's warbler nests only in young jackpine thickets in a single area of Michigan's

Lower Peninsula. What it will do if the pines are cut or burned off is a mystery. The black-footed ferret, a large and handsome weasel, preys upon prairie dogs; farmers and stock-men have destroyed most of the prairie dogs, and the ferret is now extremely hard to find.

Drainage, pollution, industrialization and the changes that it brings have ruined the habitats of many species. Breeding birds and animals establish territories to support them-selves and their hungry young, and chase other members of their species out of them; they refuse to be crowded. It wouldn't work, anyhow; there is only so much food in a given area. Also, there must be a certain number of them or they can't find each other; if there are too many males they spend their time fighting instead of mating, and the accidents of life break up too many mated pairs if there are not enough of them.

There is another class of birds that nest in colonies, and they like to jam themselves together. Most of them nest near water which is rich in marine life, so they don't need ter-ritories, but their concentrations made them very vulnerable to plume hunters, who slaughtered them mercilessly and left their young to starve. Plume hunting for women's hats went on in many places, and was so destructive that conservationists heard about it and demanded that it be stopped. This de-mand was responsible for the establishment of our first refuge, in 1903, at Pelican Island in Florida, where brown pelicans were being killed off.

In the next few years a number of ref-uges for colony-nesting birds were estab-lished. Refuges for buffalo and elk came next; and in 1908 the first refuges for ducks and

LEFT: *Millions of passenger pigeons were systematically hunted down and slaughtered. When this one bird died on September 1, 1914, in the Cincinnati Zoo, the species became extinct.*

*The Eskimo curlew was the victim of hunters in the Mississippi Valley. It is generally agreed that the bird is now extinct.*

*The exceedingly rare ivory-billed woodpecker drops out of sight for many years and then reappears amid rumors of its extinction. Its most recent sighting in North America was in 1967 in Texas's Big Thicket.*

geese were set up in Oregon and California, where millions of waterfowl concentrated at migration time. Because these areas had been drastically diminished by drainage for farming, they were set aside as refuges, and work was started to bring them back. The Malheur Refuge (page 39) is typical of this section.

Our vast original populations of ducks and geese were whittled down by shrinkage of habitat, spring shooting, and wasteful shooting by sportsmen and market hunters. In the winter of 1893, for instance, 120,000 mallards were shipped to market out of the small town of Big Lake, Arkansas, alone, and this was repeated and perhaps surpassed in many other places. Many species were almost killed off by market hunters, and ducks like the canvasbacks, redheads, and teals were not only shot by hundreds of thousands but also suffered from the drainage of prairie marshes and potholes where they nested; they were victims of progress as well as targets. The Wetlands Program (page 89) was begun in 1958 to bring back important nesting territory for them.

Among our geese, the Canada is outstanding—big, strong, sagacious, and widely distributed. Seeming to be a harbinger of spring and fall with its mellow voice and its wedges in the sky, it holds a unique place in the hearts of many people. Because of its size and delicious flavor it was almost brought low, but because it has responded so well to protection and management it has come back extremely well. Our other more widely distributed geese are the blues and greater and lesser snows. The blue goose migrates from Baffin Island to Louisiana, and great numbers of them can be seen along the Mississippi at migration time. The lesser snow goose, probably once our most abundant one, nests on Arctic islands, and spends the winter on the Gulf Coast or the coast of California; the greater snow nests in Arctic Canada and Greenland, and winters along the Maryland-Virginia-North Carolina coast. At the turn of the century the greater snow was down to two or three thousand birds; the lesser snow was slaughtered unmercifully around James Bay, where it stopped on migration. They have both increased under protection. They are lovely when they fly, with their strongly contrasting colors.

A large percentage of the refuges has been set aside for them and the other millions of our waterfowl, and are concerned with their migrations and their nesting and wintering grounds. Migration is such a complicated thing, and so necessary to understand in connection with the refuges, that it is described at some length in the following chapter.

# CHAPTER THREE

# Bird Migration and Its Importance in Conservation

In the days when much of the world was unknown, and there was more superstition than knowledge, the seasonal appearance and disappearance of birds gave rise to some amusing beliefs. Swallows were thought to plunge into the sea and spend the winter in the form of oysters; storks and other large birds took on cargoes of smaller birds and ferried them to warmer lands in the fall and back again in the spring; and birds that appeared at different times changed into each other. Many species were supposed to spend the winter in hibernation in caves and hollow trees or fly to the moon. For a long time there were acrimonious arguments between people who believed in hibernation and those who believed in migration, but the migrationists, with observation and reason on their side, finally won. Once the fact of migration was established, the routes that birds take began to be worked out.

Scientific study of migration really began with banding, the fixing of light metal rings, bearing a number for individual identification and a return address, around the legs of birds, and a Dane named Mortensen first used numbered bands around the beginning of this century. Isolated banders, such as the first ones were, don't produce much in the way of results, for a great many birds must be banded if any of them are ever to be heard of again. Organized banding, with a network of many banders and a central office to collect information, was first begun in Germany in 1901, and spread to other countries. In the United States our central banding office is at Patuxent, Maryland, and is administered by the Fish and Wildlife Service, of which the Bureau of Sport Fisheries and Wildlife is a part. Since the Bureau took over this work in 1920, something over 11,000,000 birds, of about 600 species, have been banded, and about 1,000,000 have been recovered.

Birds are banded as nestlings, or when grown are trapped, banded, and released. The band number, sex, species, and age of the bird if possible, and the time and location of the banding are registered at Patuxent. If the bird is trapped again, shot, or found dead, a report should be made or the band sent in with a note of the time and place where the bird was recovered. It is from this information, gathered little by little, that we have arrived at many of the facts about bird migration, one of the most extraordinary and mysterious events in nature. For all our investigations there are still many things hidden from us, although we have theories. We

*The bird bands used by the Fish and Wildlife Service come in fourteen sizes, from the large Canada goose band (shown here spread out) to a band for hummingbirds.*

*A bander, prepares to band ducks which have been caught with a net.*

don't know how or why these long journeys began, how many birds find their way, or why their routes vary so widely. Why does the Arctic tern fly some twenty thousand miles a year, from within 7½° of the North Pole to the Antarctic and back again? Why do those bred on the eastern side of our continent fly across the Atlantic and down the coasts of Europe and Africa, and those bred in Alaska, down the western coasts of North and South America? The blackpoll warbler and the cliff swallow are neighbors in South America in winter, but when spring comes why does the warbler fly across the Caribbean to Florida at night and the swallow fly to Panama and through Central America and Mexico in the daytime?

Many species fly different routes coming north from those they followed when they went south, and migrate at different times. A few, like the ruffed grouse, don't migrate at all, and some merely drop down in elevation; some migrate only when their food sup-

ply fails. And, although hibernation has been rather discredited, poorwills have been found in niches in the rocks in winter in a comatose condition that is very much like hibernation.

The sense of orientation, which guides birds for thousands of miles to their wintering grounds and back again to where they were hatched, also puzzles us. They must get away from winter, but how did they first find the warm places where they go? Why do some fly all the way to Patagonia from the far north when Florida would do, and why does their choice of places vary so widely? Why does the barn swallow that nests in Alaska migrate to Brazil, while the wheatears that nest in the Canadian Arctic cross the Atlantic and winter in Africa? Many fly at night or over the trackless oceans, and how do some young birds—which migrate after or before their parents—find their way to winter quarters when they have never been there before? We do know that the sun is an important reference to day-flying birds in their navigation

*The ducks are guided into a banding cage.*

*Then removed one by one for banding, and released.*

and that they have internal "clocks" to compensate for the constantly changing angle of the sun, but we don't really know how they get their bearings from it.

For a time it was thought that night-fliers—which include most of the songbirds—remembered the sun's direction when they set forth; then it was discovered that they grew confused when the night sky was overcast. This led a number of researchers to put them into planetariums or into cages from which they could see only the sky, and it was found that they navigated by the stars.

One theory, which attempts to explain why birds migrate north, has it that the increasing light of spring days gives them the mating urge and drives them north, but fails to explain why birds wintering in the Tropics leave there, where seasonal changes in daylight are imperceptible. Food is always about for birds in the Tropics, but some of them reach the north while there is still not enough to eat, and many starve. A Canadian named

Rowan caught juncos that were moving south in November and put them into outdoor cages where they were exposed to increasing amounts of electric light. They wanted to go north again to breed, but when the light was reduced, they lost this inclination. However, birds made to exercise without the increasing light acted the same way. Migration gives birds their maximum exercise, but after their long flights south, where many of them enjoy a second spring, they don't breed.

One of the most remarkable things about migration is its regularity, and in many cases the days birds reach certain points on their way can be predicted. They don't all do this; Canada geese, for instance, move according to temperature. It is also interesting that many migrating birds held captive for a time lose their urge to migrate farther.

The routes that birds follow on their mysterious travels in the Western Hemisphere are basically north and south, but within this axis there are infinite variations

29

in direction and width of migration path. The Ipswich sparrow, for instance, is never far from the surf along the Atlantic Coast; the redstart's path to Mexico and South America is over two thousand miles wide. Despite such variations we know that most species follow four main routes on their journeys. These great highways of the air are called flyways, and are shown on the accompanying maps. They were discovered by Frederick C. Lincoln of the Biological Survey in 1935 from a study of bands recovered from migrating waterfowl, and this information enabled us to draw maps showing where birds come from, the routes they follow, and where they go, and enabled us to locate the best places for refuges. The flyways are not clearly defined and sometimes cross or intersect each other; some birds with wide breeding areas, like the canvasback duck, will use different flyways or even all four. Besides these, there are two routes over the oceans, like the Pacific golden plover's flight to Hawaii and the Atlantic golden plover's flight down the Atlantic from Nova Scotia to the Brazilian coast, but not many species use them because of the long, perilous flights over the open sea where there are no landmarks. Many birds stray from their routes and are found in places where they don't belong; like the rest of us, they just get lost.

A comparatively few waterfowl refuges where concentrations are really spectacular, such as Tule Lake, Bear River, the Klamath Basin, Upper Mississippi, and Malheur, had been established before 1935, but they couldn't be called a refuge system. With the knowledge of waterfowl movements that the flyway conception revealed, we could plan a series of refuges that would be like a series of stepping-stones along the flyways where mi-grating birds could find sanctuary and food. They needed such places, for by the early thirties the long drought that produced the Dust Bowl had dried up a great deal of their nesting territory, and hunting bag limits were so high that they had gone into a disastrous decline. In those days there was no Migratory Bird Populations Station, such as the one at Patuxent now, to keep tabs on them and set bag limits to prevent overshooting.

As the system was expanded and waterfowl populations rose again, it appeared that the birds didn't have enough protection at the American end of the flyways. The stepping-stones were working well, but the birds stepped off them into nothing, and so wintering refuges began to be added where protection and good feeding were available during the winter in the southern states. This was very good but not good enough, for drainage in the northern prairie states continued until 100,000,000 acres of prime nesting territory was gone, and then another long drought came along that took much of the nesting territory that was left. There was another disastrous decline in waterfowl populations, and this led to the Wetlands Program (page 89), which was designed to prevent the draining of all our prairie nesting territory.

In the years of trouble and great waterfowl decline, the refuge people were so busy fighting disaster that they didn't welcome visitors to the refuges. Now that things are better and conservation has made such large strides forward, their thinking has changed. They believe that more and more outdoor recreation of high quality should be made available to people who are really interested in it, and steps are being taken with this in mind. The Bureau wants people to know this, and to know that they will be welcomed to refuges.

30

RIGHT ABOVE: *The golden plover, once nearly extinct, has been restored in number.*

RIGHT: *The black-necked stilt must bend its long red legs in order to reach its food.*

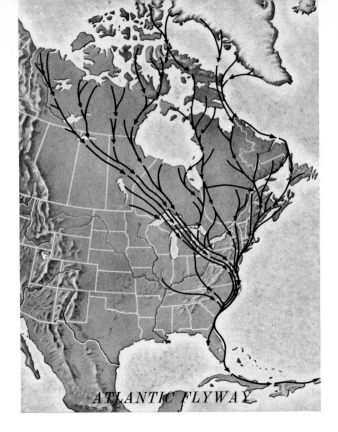

*ATLANTIC FLYWAY*

*MISSISSIPPI FLYWAY*

## FLYWAYS:
THE ROUTES BIRDS TAKE

*The Atlantic Flyway* follows the Atlantic Coast. From the top of Maine to the southernmost tip of Florida, it is almost 1,800 miles long. It has one of the densest human populations in the nation, but it also has a vast amount of unoccupied space in it.

Waterfowl from the northeast side of the continent, the Canadian prairies, Baffin Island, and the eastern Arctic use it. Although it holds more than a third of the wetlands in the country, only about 12 percent of this area is very good for waterfowl because of the things that have been done to it. It is used by about 15 percent of our migrating ducks and 20 percent of the geese.

The Middle Atlantic States have the greatest diversity of waterfowl. Many come to that section from the prairie states without passing through the northern end of the flyway. They cut across below the Great Lakes.

*The Mississippi Flyway* follows the Mississippi drainage to the Gulf Coast. It is used by waterfowl from the prairie states and provinces (where probably 50 percent of our ducks are hatched), the delta of the Mackenzie, and Alaska, across the continent to Hudson Bay and Baffin Island. It is our most important flyway, tapping our best waterfowl breeding grounds. Eight million ducks, geese, swans, and coots winter along it, and many move through it to winter farther south.

A great number of very productive marshes and potholes that once produced ducks have been drained, but waterfowl are resilient and have learned to take advantage of the new refuges, reservoirs, and the vast increase in grain farming and farm ponds. Geese, in particular, have responded wonderfully to the man-made changes.

One of the main points of worry on this flyway is weather. Drought cycles can severely interfere with nesting success, and too much rain at the wrong time drowns out many nests. As this is primarily nesting habitat country, a great deal of work is being done to improve the habitat that is left and to expand it if we can.

*The Central Flyway* starts in Alaska and western Canada and follows east of the Rocky Mountains down through the Great Plains to the Gulf of Mexico. It is wide and roomy,

*CENTRAL FLYWAY*

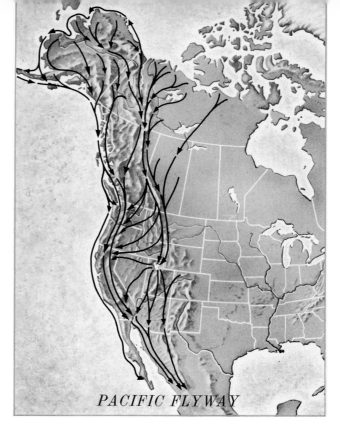

*PACIFIC FLYWAY*

running westward from the pothole country to mountain valleys which have plenty of water in the form of streams and beaver dams.

Much of the flyway is semiarid. In years of drought its production, like the Mississippi Flyway's, declines dramatically, but in good years it hatches a lot of ducks. Mallards and pintails are the most numerous dabbling ducks; blue-winged teal are probably the most numerous nesters; and redheads are the most numerous divers. The western Canada goose is predominant, and sometimes the giant Canada appears. The trumpeter swan is at present confined primarily to this flyway.

Watershed protection programs and the construction of hundreds of thousands of acres of stock ponds and runoff detention reservoirs have made up for some of the drainage done on this flyway. Tidal marshes extending along the Texas coast from Matagorda Bay winter about 45 percent of the ducks and 90 percent of the geese. A great deal of rice is grown in the northern part of this country.

*The Pacific Flyway* stretches from the crest of the Rockies to the Pacific Ocean, and from the northern Alaskan coast into Mexico. Most of it is in either arid country or mountainous country. Rainfall is low over a large part of it, and hydroelectric power and irrigation for extensive farming and fruit growing have made great demands on the water. The great agricultural development sometimes causes problems when hungry waterfowl by the hundreds of thousands descend upon the farms.

Ducks and geese that breed in vast numbers in Alaska and Canada find their best wintering grounds in the Sacramento–San Joaquin Valley, the Klamath Basin, and the Columbia River watershed. Many others go on to the less crowded and wilder lakes and lagoons of Mexico.

As in other flyways, mallards are the most widely distributed ducks. In the north, pintails are the most numerous nesters. There are snow, Ross', and white-fronted geese and four subspecies of Canadas.

California leads in wintering birds, having an average of 4,000,000 ducks over the last ten years. Washington comes next, with 740,000 ducks, and Oregon winters half a million. Idaho winters about 100,000.

# *The Refuges*

*At Malheur, common egrets
search the marsh for crayfish,
fishes, tadpoles, insects,
and other foods.
They nest in colonies.*

*From their vantage point in a juniper,
two young ferruginous hawks keep a watchful eye
on the sagebrush-covered plains of Malheur.*

# The Northwest

Region One of the National Wildlife Refuge System includes the West Coast states, Montana, Idaho, Nevada, Alaska, and the Leeward Islands off Hawaii. It is administered from Portland, Oregon. Taking in such a wide and varied territory, it has a greater variety of wildlife than any other region. Most of the waterfowl migrating through the Pacific Flyway or nesting along it use these refuges, and there are a number of them for seabirds that nest in colonies along the coast. There are also a number of refuges for large animals. Such refuges as Sacramento, Colusa, and Sutter, all in the Sacramento Valley, although limited in size, are very important for wintering waterfowl and often hold hundreds of thousands of ducks and geese from September until late in the winter. The Klamath Basin complex of refuges, clustered along the Oregon-California border, contains an area of 121,000 acres, and in October, the peak of the season, holds millions of waterfowl—the greatest concentration on the continent. The Charles M. Russell National Wildlife Range in Montana occupies a 220-mile stretch along the Missouri River, and provides habitat for sharp-tailed and sage grouse, turkeys, pronghorn, elk, deer, bighorn sheep, and waterfowl. The Desert National Wildlife Range in Nevada contains two million acres, is bisected by U.S. Highway 95, and is fascinating for its desert plants, birds, and mammals.

*At Malheur Refuge in Oregon
one can see large numbers of sandhill cranes
and view their spectacular
mating dances. These four-foot-tall birds
put on a show that would be hard to
equal in the natural world.*

*Rocky mountain bighorn sheep gather on the high slopes of the Bison Range in Montana.*

The volcanic Cascade Range, running north and south, divides Oregon into a soft, pleasant land of vast forests with high rainfall along the Pacific Coast and high desert and mountains in the interior. The desert in the southeastern quarter of the state encompasses immense distances of stunted juniper and sagebrush, grim mountains, and seemingly endless plateaus of bare, dark rimrock; driving through it is like sailing on a lonely gray-green sea bounded by bleak flat tablelands of buttes running to the horizon.

The Malheur National Wildlife Refuge, one of our oldest, and very important in the Pacific Flyway, is in this country. It covers 181,000 acres, and has two big lakes and one smaller one fed by the Blitzen and Silvies rivers. The lakes are shallow and have no outlets. Malheur Lake, the largest, covers 45,-000 acres and is really a vast marsh with areas of open water. The valley of the Blitzen, running for thirty-five miles between the tablelands, holds a multitude of managed ponds, marshes, and meadows. This valley and Malheur Lake between them make one of the most important nesting areas and migration stops for waterfowl and shorebirds in the refuge system. In years of good rain and snowfall, the refuge can produce 30,000 ducklings.

Refuge headquarters is a pretty complex of buildings among which there is a good small museum, and near it a road running out on the long Cole Island Dike into Malheur Lake. Out there is a reedy world broken by patches of open water, where in good years there are always ducks and geese on the water or in the air, a few trumpeter swans brought in from Red Rock Lakes, and an enormous

array of other birds that a good marsh attracts. Most abundant nesters among the ducks are gadwalls, cinnamon teal, mallards, and redheads. At the height of spring and fall migrations there are from a quarter to a half million ducks on the refuge. Twenty-six species of shore and marsh birds appear on the refuge, and Malheur is one of the best refuges in the system to watch and photograph the extraordinary mating dances of sandhill cranes from a blind built for the purpose. Five species of owls, four of hawks, and golden eagles nest here; all in all, 248 species of birds have been seen at one time or another on the refuge. It is a great pleasure to watch the ducks on the water or scaling down through the air, and western grebes, white pelicans, Forster's and black terns, and yellow-headed blackbirds are always in evidence. When we were there, there was a horned owl nesting in a wire basket in a tree near headquarters, and as we stopped to look at it it stared back at us haughtily, as though to ask us where else it would nest in a country where trees were scarce and hollow trees practically nonexistent.

From the owl's nest we turned up the valley of the Blitzen, where the water is manipulated with dams, dikes, and canals to make as many ponds and marshy meadows as possible. Most of the ponds held ducks with housekeeping in mind, many of them being handsome cinnamon teal, and Canada geese were nesting on top of muskrat houses. As we paused to look at them, they lay very low and stretched their necks flat on the houses for concealment.

After a short detour to look at some

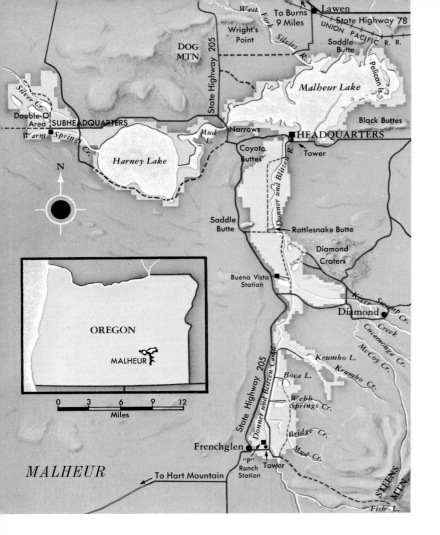

To Hart Mountain

MALHEUR

OREGON

MALHEUR

0  3  6  9  12
Miles

They have increased nicely under protection —much better than the whooping cranes, for which they were sometimes mistaken by early travelers.

John Scharff, the refuge manager, wanted to show us a nesting golden eagle, so we left the marshes and went off toward a butte in the desert. Presently, we saw an eagle in the air, carrying a snake. He hovered over the edge of the butte and we saw the nest under him. It was a huge pile of sticks about twelve feet high and twelve feet from the top of the butte, and the female eagle was sitting on it. She looked oddly earthbound, patiently enduring a sort of captivity away from the great heights that were her heritage. She didn't seem to belong there, and I recalled other eagles: one screaming so high above me on top of the Rockies as to be out of sight above the peaks, and another plummeting down a mountainside with dark wings backed and the air roaring past.

Her mate reappeared high above the butte and dropped down and slid past her to drop the snake beside her on the nest, and then soared up out of sight. "During my thirty-one years here," Mr. Scharff said, "that nest has never been unoccupied, but I don't know whether it's been the same pair of eagles or not."

Few white men got into the region until the 1850s, when gold miners on the way from California to new diggings in Idaho crossed it; their reports of the fine grass and abundant game brought ranchers and others in. A little later, the mop-up began. Plume hunters, market hunters, and settlers between them slaughtered hundreds of thousands of birds for their feathers or for food, and many thousands of beaver, otter, mink, and muskrat skins were taken out. As the settlers increased, they diverted the streams to irrigate hayfields, and the levels of the lakes dropped until one of the greatest waterfowl areas in

ancient Indian pictographs on a boulder, we turned off the road to drive along the tops of the canal dikes to get into the middle of the marshes. In a big grassy water meadow, a sandhill crane appeared in the distance, and staggered off, giving all the signs of injury and distress. She had a nest there with eggs in it, and was trying to lead us away from it. We saw more of them as we drove along, scattered pairs already nested or about to nest. Tall, grayish birds with bald red crowns and tufted tails typical of the cranes, with a wingspread of six or seven feet, they are strong fliers and migrate long distances. Their range runs from Siberia and Alaska to Texas and central Mexico. Once they were very numerous; they were overshot by hunters, for they came readily to decoys.

*Mule deer differ from the Eastern whitetails by having a black tail tip and a black patch on their foreheads.*

*The Blitzen Valley is dotted with shallow lakes and ponds, such as this one, which serve as valuable duck breeding areas.*

*Golden eagles are large brown birds with golden nape feathers. They establish large hunting territories and drive out other hawks and eagles that might compete with them for food.*

*A sandhill crane stands over her nest in the reeds, where she is incubating two eggs. These birds are rare in the East, but are still numerous in western United States.*

the United States was reduced to a fraction of its former size. In 1908 President Roosevelt set aside Harney and Malheur lakes as the Lake Malheur Reservation; the area was enlarged by President Hoover, the Blitzen Valley lands were added by President Franklin Roosevelt in 1935, and in 1940 the reservation became the Malheur National Wildlife Refuge.

Bighorn sheep were once found on the refuge, but, like the otters, are there no longer. There are still coyotes, bobcats, beavers, muskrats, and a small population of pronghorns; mule deer are most numerous in the fall. Porcupines come in winter, blacktail jack rabbits race automobiles, and there are ten species of bats; among the other animals are such interesting species as kangaroo rats, whitetail antelope squirrels, bushy-tailed wood rats, and spotted skunks.

The Klamath Basin National Wildlife Refuges are not very far from Malheur and are similar to it in their topography and purpose. They are a complex consisting of Upper Klamath, Lower Klamath, Klamath Forest, Tule Lake, and Clear Lake refuges, administered from one headquarters and between them covering 112,589 acres in southern Oregon and northern California. Ducks and geese from the great prairie provinces of Canada, the far reaches of Alaska, Malheur, Bear River—the majority of birds of the Pacific Flyway—funnel into the basin in spring and fall, and at the height of migration their numbers scattered around the basin may come close to 7,000,000—the greatest concentration of waterfowl on the continent.

As settlers came in and increased, drainage, diversion of water, and farming took away much of the 400,000 acres of splendid waterfowl habitat, but the birds returned to it just the same, crowded into what was left, and, not finding enough to eat, descended upon the farmers' crops. Great damage was done, but that wasn't the end of it; from the basin the ducks went on down to the Sacramento Valley where an immense amount of rice is grown, and into the Imperial Valley where there is much lettuce farming. Hungry ducks love rice and lettuce, and millions of them can make terrible inroads upon it. There was an understandable uproar, and something had to be done. The areas now in refuges were brought back with water-control measures, and became in a way farming operations to hold the birds until the farmers harvested their crops. At Tule Lake alone,

2,500 acres are planted in grain crops for ducks, and additional land in grass for geese.

The headquarters of the complex are at Tule Lake, probably the most important refuge in the system, for at times there are 4,000,000 birds upon it—more than at any other refuge. The original area of the lake has been greatly reduced, but it grows an enormous amount of aquatic food plants. Gadwalls, mallards, redheads, cinnamon teal, ruddy ducks, and Canada geese are the most abundant nesters; millions of pintails and other ducks nesting farther north go through, as well as over half a million cackling, white-fronted, and snow geese. The best time to see and photograph all these birds is in late October.

Most of the nesting Canadas in the basin are Great Basin Canadas, one of the fifteen subspecies of a clan that in its ramifications covers most of the North American continent. They vary greatly in size, although all of them are unmistakable in their appearance. The large ones are the giant Canadas, running up to twenty pounds, and the Atlantic Canadas, running up to eleven. The smaller subspecies run from the lesser Canadas, weighing up to eight pounds, ranging from the Gulf Coast to the Arctic Ocean, to the three- to four-pound cackling Canadas which nest in Alaska and winter in California, and the little Aleutian Canadas that seldom leave the Aleutians. The only known breeding population of these small geese is on Buldir Island, where there are no foxes to destroy their nests.

The Canadas we know best, of course,

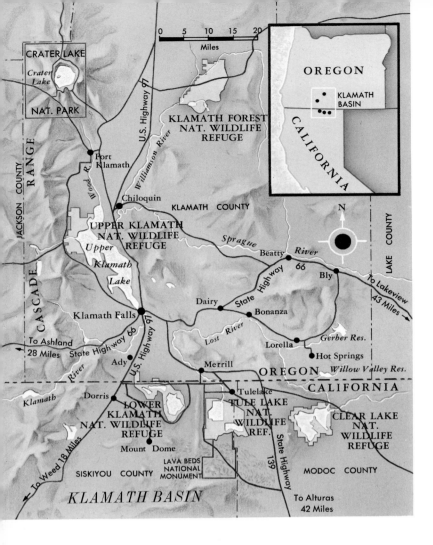

are the Atlantic or continental Canadas, that move across the sky in their wedges and arouse more affection, wanderlust, or hunters' excitement than any other bird. Intelligent, faithful all their lives to their mates, and model parents, they were once brought very low by overhunting. They have responded wonderfully to protection and management, and seem to have a bright future. I have been told that there are now more geese at the Seney Refuge in Michigan than there were at one time in the whole Mississippi Flyway.

*Clear Lake supports the largest colony of white pelicans in the United States. The pelican scrapes up a mound of sandy soil about six inches high to support its nest.*

44

*Crops raised at Sacramento National Wildlife Refuge lure migrating waterfowl in the Pacific Flyway and help to keep the birds from eating rice and lettuce fields farther south.*

*Conspicuous marks of identification of western Canada geese are the black neck and white "chin strap," which are common to all subspecies of Canadas.*

This increase, as well as some changed ideas of the geese themselves, has brought a problem. Once they all flew south for the winter, but now many of them don't bother to go so far any more. The mechanical corn-picker, which leaves a lot of corn in the fields, has changed their patterns of migration; now a great many of them stay and live all winter on it. Some localities where goose shooting used to be good now have none at all, and some which had no goose shooting now have plenty of it. The consequence of this is a number of unhappy and vocal goose hunters and people who profited from them who want the situation changed. They should probably talk to the geese, which, more than themselves, have kept up with progress and the changes that it brings.

# Bison Range

Half of Montana is a mile or more above the sea, but only a third of the state is mountainous, and in this region you are never out of sight of mountains. Many gleam with snow most of the year, and the Indians called this country The Land of the Shining Mountains. It has beautiful forests and lakes and thousands of miles of trout streams that are never crowded. Many of the valleys are flat and wide, and the National Bison Range is on the edge of one of them, near the Mission Range. It would be harder to find a more handsome range of mountains than the Missions, which rise like a wall to 10,300 feet at their highest point, rugged and snow-topped. There is a fine variety of trees in this country: alpine and Douglas fir, Engelmann spruce, limber, lodgepole, and ponderosa pine, western larch and balsam. Shrubs, flowering plants, and grasses flourish, for the climate is pleasant and there is adequate rainfall.

The Bison Range holds 18,540 acres of steep rolling hills covered with native bunchgrass and small forests of Douglas fir and ponderosa pine. There is a difference of 2,300 feet between the low point at refuge headquarters and the top of Highpoint Lookout, where there is a magnificent view of the valley, the Missions, and the distant Bitterroot Range to the west. The Lookout is on the self-guided auto tour, open from June 1 through September 30, over a good gravel road; the route is about nineteen miles long and can be completed in two hours, but the visitor may take all day if he wishes, winding around the hills to pause and look at the lovely views and watch the many animals and birds of the refuge.

There were only about twenty wild buffalo left in the United States when President Theodore Roosevelt obtained an appropriation from Congress to buy and fence the Bison Range. The fencing was necessary in an area without natural boundaries where there is a good deal of ranching, for buffalo and ranching don't mix. A series of interior fences are an aid in handling them as well as the other big-game animals, the elk, mule and white-tailed deer, pronghorns, and bighorn sheep. These fences don't make the refuge seem like a zoo; with the long, long views and the free-ranging animals one forgets them.

The day we took our tour with the refuge manager, we wound around the hills, paused on the Lookout to see the view, and started down. Far below, tiny and dark in the distance, were buffalo, and we wanted to get close to them. Part way down, around a shoulder, we came upon a herd of ten buck antelope. They are used to being looked at, and sometimes they race cars for the fun of it. This time they drew together, watched us for a time, and moved off. They had had a delicate elegance standing still; in motion they had a flowing grace.

Presently, we were down on the flat among the buffalo. There were several reddish, awkward calves, one or two of the cows gave us a stare, but the big brown bulls chose to ignore us. They moved slowly past us, and we thought of the time when millions of them lived on the Plains and when the Indians, before they had horses or guns, stampeded great herds over cliffs for their winter meat supply, or later ran them for many miles with

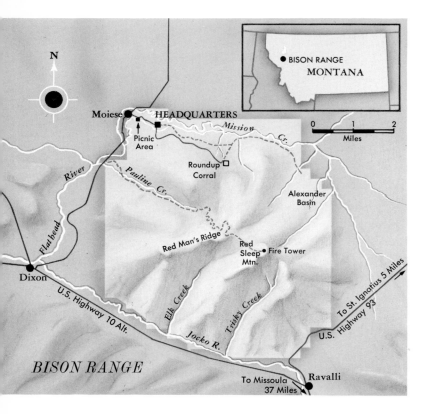

*The grizzly bear, now rare in the contiguous forty-eight states, is probably most numerous in the remote Missions and the Northern Cascades. It has fared better in Alaska.*

specially trained horses, and lanced or shot them at a gallop—a stirring and dangerous enterprise.

They are hardy beasts, able to stand almost any weather, and their bones have been found on peaks where men had to leave horses behind and climb on foot; their only real enemies were the Indians and the buffalo, or "loafer," wolf, and they could contend with these things. It was the white man who brought them very close to extinction. It saddened me to think of this as the sunlight lay golden on their backs and softened their outlines when we turned away to leave them.

We saw no mule deer, which usually stay on the ridges, or elk, which usually stay in timber. A little later we took a side trip into bighorn sheep country and thought we might see some of them on the high, rocky south side of the range. They are easy to approach here, and many good pictures of them have been taken, but they were somewhere else that day. We did, however, see several golden eagles soaring majestically on the rising air currents. They made up for some of our disappointment. Who wouldn't forget some of the big-game animals for a time to watch an eagle wheeling in the sky?

There aren't many whitetail jack rabbits on the Range anymore, although they were once numerous in the valley. Snowshoe hares stay in the timber; striped skunks, mink, and muskrats are fairly common, and occasionally one sees a badger. Coyotes aren't common, owing to somewhat dubious control measures everywhere but on the range. Black bears appear a few times to gorge on the thorn apples along the creek bottoms, and there are grizzlies in the wilderness of the Missions; it is probably their point of highest concentration outside the National Parks and Alaska.

One hundred and seventy-one species of birds have been identified on the range, among them Lewis' woodpeckers, Clark's nutcrackers, western tanagers, and blue

*The albino bull, leader of the Bison Range herd*
*until his death in 1959, stands out*
*in sharp contrast to his darker counterpart.*

grouse; ring-necked pheasants, gray partridges, and chukars are common.

Forty buffalo were sent to the range in 1909 after the fencing was completed, and the composition of this herd is interesting because it shows how far it was necessary to go to find buffalo in private herds even at that time. Thirty-four were bought and two were donated from the Conrad herd at Kalispell, Montana, which had originally been started by a Pend d'Oreille Indian who had brought four calves back from a hunting expedition; one came from the Goodnight herd in Texas, and three from the Corbin herd in New Hampshire. These herds, along with four others scattered over the country, were started by men who didn't want to see the buffalo vanish from the face of the earth, and most of the buffalo we have today came from them.

The largest American herd, at Custer State Park in South Dakota, numbers 1,300 animals, and there is now a herd in Alaska. Three white calves were born there within the last few years, but none of them is alive now.

White buffalo have always been very rare, and of the five white calves reported in government herds in the last sixty years, two were born on the Bison Range. One was Big Medicine, twenty-six years old when he died in 1959; he was all white with the exception of the top of his head, which was brown. The other was his son. Big Medicine may have been the ancestor of the Alaskan white calves, for the Alaskan buffalo came from the Bison Range.

The Indians thought that white buffalo were sacred, and belonged to the sun. If they killed one, they didn't use the meat; the tongue was dried, the hide carefully tanned, and both were ceremoniously tied to the center pole of an abandoned lodge and left to weather back to the earth again. No passing Indian would disturb them.

Two sons of the French explorer Pierre Gaultier de Varennes de la Vérendrye were

*A herd of bison crosses
the Mission River
on the northern edge
of the Bison Range.
By mid-June,
their thick winter coats
have been shed.*

probably the first white men to reach Montana, in 1743; sixty years later the Lewis and Clark party passed through the country, and their descriptions of it caused Manuel Lisa, one of the mountain men, to ascend the Yellowstone River to the mouth of the Bighorn where he established Lisa's Fort, Montana's first fur post. In 1807 Lisa sent out an exploring party; one of its members was John Colter, who, after escaping from the Blackfeet who had captured him, found "Colter's Hell"—a weird region of geysers and hot springs which is now Yellowstone Park. The American Fur Company started the first

permanent settlement at Fort Benton, on the Missouri, in 1847. The St. Ignatius Mission, near the Bison Range, was established by the Jesuits in 1854. It is still there, and probably the only mission left in that country from those days. Gold was discovered in the state in 1856; thousands of prospectors came crowding in, and Indian troubles began. There were fights and massacres, and the Sioux under Sitting Bull wiped out Custer's command at the Little Bighorn in 1876. There was great lawlessness for a time; but finally ranchers, farmers, and railroads came in, and Montana became a state in 1889.

One hundred and fifty miles or so northwest of Niihau, the most westerly of the principal Hawaiian Islands, lies the 146-acre islet of Nihoa, a volcanic peak standing nearly nine hundred feet above the Pacific. It is the first of a series of islets, shoals, reefs, and pinnacles that extend westward for over a thousand miles, and are called the Leeward Islands. Their base is a sunken volcanic ridge capped in places with coral, and the sea is very deep around them. Their climate, like Hawaii's, is one of the pleasantest in the world. Most of them are low and sandy, all of them are small; the largest, Laysan, about two-thirds of the way out the chain, is only two square miles in area. All of them but two are in the Hawaiian Islands National Wildlife Refuge, upon which nobody lives.

The remoteness and isolation of the Leewards produced species which are found nowhere else, and attract some of the greatest sea-bird colonies in the world. Hundreds of thousands of Laysan and black-footed albatrosses, wedge-tailed and Christmas Island shearwaters, frigate birds, and numerous species of petrels, boobies, tropic birds, and terns come in from their far wanderings over the vast areas of the world's largest ocean to nest, particularly upon Laysan. The island also held resident birds—a duck, a flightless rail, a honey creeper, a finch, and a miller bird —that were unique. It was a paradise for ornithologists; but before the twentieth century began, hunters who supplied the millinery trade with feathers for women's hats slaughtered countless thousands of nesting birds, and the manager of a guano shipping company introduced rabbits for food in 1904.

Some of the rabbits escaped, and having no enemies to keep them in check increased until they were destroying the island's vegetation.

Protests by scientists and conservationists led President Roosevelt to establish a refuge in 1909, and this took care of the feather hunters; but it was not until 1923 that the rabbits were exterminated, and by that time the island was practically a barren waste. The unique rails, miller birds, and honey creepers, having no more insect life to feed upon or any place to nest, vanished from the earth. The pretty Laysan teal, down to seven birds in 1911, has managed to come back; there were 600 of them in 1963, and they are still the world's rarest duck. Many of the plants, as unique as the birds, also disappeared; the rest have gradually come back in a measure. All this is a classic example of what happens when an ill-considered change is made by man in a biotic community that was in balance.

Laysan is a bowl-shaped, low island with a lagoon in the center; reefs and coral ledges surround it, and it has areas of ocher-colored beach. The Hawaiian monk seal, seen only in the Leewards, is found here, and there are green sea turtles up to four feet in diameter. Golden plover, bristle-thighed curlew, ruddy turnstones, and wandering tattlers, which breed in Alaska, winter on the island. Such birds as Siberian whimbrels, red phalaropes, and black-bellied plover, some of which migrate from Siberia or Alaska to New Zealand and back, stop at Laysan. And occasionally mallards and other ducks are seen. It is almost unbelievable that these birds can find the tiny island in the vast, empty reaches of the sea. It is even more remarkable that the oceanic birds that nest here can find it, for they wander all over the Pacific.

Well over a quarter of a million black-footed and Laysan albatrosses may be on Laysan between August and late October. They are big birds with seven-foot wing-spreads, beautiful fliers whose effortless, gliding flight has always fascinated observers. They go through extraordinary antics in their courting. Sooty, grayback, and fairy terns nest on Laysan; the sooties alone far outnumber the albatrosses; the graybacks lay eggs with pink yolks, and the lovely little fairy terns—almost transparent and ghostlike against the brilliant sky—lay their eggs on a rock or a horizontal tree limb, to which the young bird must cling until it can fly.

Also among the nesters are white-capped, brown, and blue-gray noddies, beautiful red-

*Nihoa, a volcanic peak, is included in the Hawaiian Islands National Wildlife Refuge.*

*The two-square-mile island of Laysan, which has an inland lagoon, is the largest island in the Hawaiian Islands Refuge.*

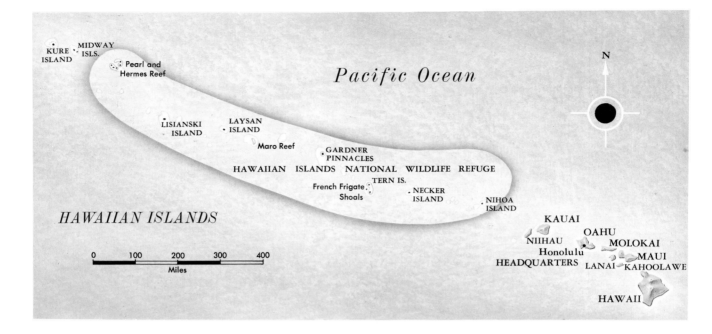

*The brown booby, shown here with its white chick on the southeast island of Pearl and Hermes Reef, is the most wide-ranging of the booby tribe. Boobies get their name from the ease with which they are caught.*

tailed tropic birds, and blue-faced, brown, and masked boobies. These last are robbed by the frigate birds, probably the most expert fliers of all; male frigates have great bright-red inflated throat pouches in the mating season. The old Hawaiians used to tame them and use them as messengers, like carrier pigeons, when they were away from home.

Perhaps the strangest of all the nesting seafarers are the wedge-tailed and Christmas Island shearwaters and the Bonin, Bulwer's, and sooty storm petrels. They fly and feed at night, flitting eerily about, and squeal, squall, moan, or sound like growling kittens or fighting cats. They make burrows in the sand where they spend the days and lay their eggs, and in the days when the vegetation had been destroyed and there was nothing to stabilize the sand, it blew about and buried great numbers of them in their burrows.

Not all the birds nest at the same time, but roughly in sequence, and in season the air and the Island is full of them. They are extraordinarily tame, for they have had little contact with man and don't fear him. Fairy terns, hovering before a man's face, may be

54

RIGHT ABOVE: *Laysan albatrosses do a courtship dance.*
RIGHT: *In the mating season the frigate bird has a gular pouch.*
FAR RIGHT: *The Laysan finch inhabits both Laysan and Nihoa.*

*Among the world's rarest birds, the Nihoa miller bird lives on that island and nowhere else. It is believed that this was the first nest of this species ever found on Nihoa.*

*A Hawaiian monk seal and her pups come ashore on a refuge beach. The total population of these seals is no more than a thousand.*

caught in the hand; petrels have climbed into men's laps and looked curiously at them, and when there were rails on Laysan they ran unconcerned about people's feet. Albatrosses may be stroked sitting on their nests, and most of the other birds can be closely approached. Unfortunately, the feather hunters merely had to walk up to them and knock them on the head.

Few ships pass in sight of the Leewards now, and written permission is necessary to land on the refuge. Great care is taken that no harmful species of birds, animals, or plants are brought ashore. The main islands of Hawaii have lost twenty-seven of the seventy native species since 1778, in the face of the march we call progress, and nineteen more are now considered to be in danger. The Leewards have been brought back into balance, and it is hoped that we can keep them that way.

# The Alaskan Refuges

The Alaskan refuges are extraordinary in their wild beauty, their size, and the wildlife that they hold. Nowhere else in the nation can one find moose of such dimensions, big brown bears, polar bears, caribou, musk ox, walrus, reindeer, or refuges that are measured in thousands of square miles and hold so many glaciers, soaring and rugged mountains, volcanoes, vast marshes or lonely, stormy seas.

Alaska is a land of few roads, where everyone gets around by air, and many of the refuges are difficult to reach and have little or nothing in the way of accommodation when you get there. Weather isn't very dependable, and some of the flying in light planes isn't for the apprehensive.

There are seventeen Alaskan refuges, running in size from the forty-two acres of Hazy Island, a sea-bird rookery off the coast of southern Alaska, to the 8,900,000-acre Arctic Refuge in the northeast corner of the state. We shall take up three of them at some length, Kenai, Kodiak, and Nunivak National Wildlife Refuges.

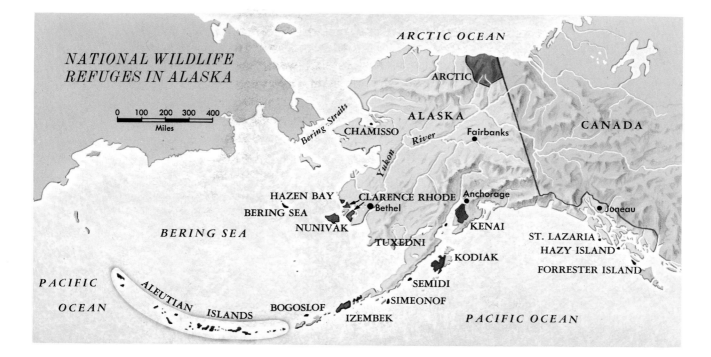

NATIONAL WILDLIFE REFUGES IN ALASKA

The Kenai National Moose Range, lying 160 miles by road from Anchorage, combines within its 2,700 square miles a splendid and accessible recreation area which supports over 7,000 of the world's largest moose as well as big brown and black bears, Dall's sheep, mountain goats, and a variety of smaller animals in the way of beaver, mink, lynx, coyotes, a few wolves, hoary marmots, and wolverines in the wildest reaches; 146 species of birds have been identified on the refuge, including the rare trumpeter swans. Two-thirds of the refuge is lowland, with rolling hills and muskeg, much of it timbered with spruce, aspen, willow, and birch; there are over 1,200 lakes, 160 miles of rivers, and many smaller streams. The remaining third is in the Kenai Mountains, which rise to 6,612 feet and on their heights contain the great Harding Ice Field from which a number of tributary glaciers wind their way down the valleys. The two largest lakes, Tustumena and Skilak, are larger than many refuges in the contiguous states, between them covering about 97,000 acres. There are many miles of good access roads on Kenai and over a dozen maintained camping sites, some with boat ramps, all planned to give campers as much privacy as possible.

Before the end of the nineteenth century, there were more caribou than moose on Kenai, but several extensive fires destroyed great areas of caribou moss, which they feed upon, and their numbers declined until by 1912 there were none left. Conditions for them have improved since then, and they are being reintroduced.

The fires that wiped out so much caribou habitat were the best thing that could have happened to the moose, for they are browsers, and the plants and young trees that come up after fires furnish large amounts of browse for a time, and it is browse that carried them through the winters. In summer they are much in the water, feeding on the roots of aquatic plants. The dominant tree on Kenai is spruce, and there is controlled lumbering to keep the spruce from taking over everything and bringing the moose herd into a decline.

Besides the camping spots, there are two chains of wilderness lakes laid out for canoe routes. The lakes are all wild and pretty, and portages between them are usually short. Wildlife can be observed from them, and the fishing for Dolly Varden, rainbow, and steelhead trout is excellent; where they empty into the refuge rivers there is also fine fishing for red, silver, king, chum, and pink salmon. Most of the lakes are small and protected by forest, and rough water is seldom a problem. The Swanson River canoe route links more than forty lakes, and can be covered in its entirety by canoes or outboard-motored boats in less than a week, if one wants to go the entire length. The Swan Lake canoe route is about sixty miles long, and can be covered in about the same time; it contains many lakes, and eventually empties into the Moose River. These canoe routes can be reached by access roads in several places, and are popular with people who want to get away from the campgrounds and into the wilderness.

One day the refuge manager flew me over the refuge in a light floatplane. We covered

Barren ground caribou often bed down in a patch of snow, where the reflection of light apparently discourages bothersome insects.

The wolverine, one of North America's rarest mammals, is one of the strongest and most vicious. Wolverines are most at home in the barren tundra of Canada and Alaska.

a lot of the lowland first, flying at about a thousand feet or less, and could see a great deal. There were literally dozens of moose on the muskegs or along the shores of the lakes, many of them huge bulls with horns still in the velvet.

Finally, we swung toward the mountains, and the ground began to rise. We followed the valley of the Russian River, milky with silt and rock flour from the glacier where it rises; the valley grew narrower and wilder, and presently we were above timberline where the precipitous slopes were green and tundralike. We turned into another valley, and the first thing we saw was a pair of big brown bears on the slope; they stood together and watched us pass. Then we began to see little bunches of Dall's sheep, white on the green slopes that seemed almost perpendicular, some of them at the top of rock faces that dropped straight down for over a thousand

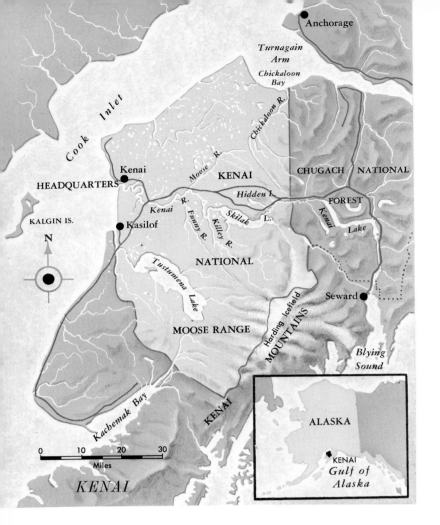

*In winter, Arctic foxes are entirely white except for a few black hairs at the tip of the tail. The blue phase is a Maltese color. These curious foxes will follow a man around.*

feet and were lost in the clouds below. We also passed a bunch of goats, which moved about more deliberately than the sheep.

We left that valley and turned back to the foot of the glacier, and soon the glacier was below us, blue and crackled, a great frozen river winding up to the Harding Ice Field among peaks fragmentary in clouds and cold mists. We ascended the glacier until the mists began to close in around us, turned low over a rocky shoulder, and wound our way through the peaks until we came to a high tundra lake and landed on it. We tied the plane to a dwarf willow and took a walk on the tundra.

In that high silent world a thin carpeting of tundra flowers were in blossom, and the footing was as soft as a cushion. Two young hoary marmots whistled at us from atop a rock, and disappeared. We walked for a time among the bright lichens and caribou moss and tiny flowers, wondering how long it had been since anyone else had walked in that bleak and lovely place, and then went back to the plane again, took off, and wound our way through the peaks to the glacier and down to the Russian River again and so back to the lowlands. The world was flat again, after the high, bald shoulders, the sharp misty peaks and the blue glacier, the plunging mountainsides, the eagles and the sheep.

The climate of Kenai is sub-Arctic, falling as low as 40 degrees below zero in winter; summers are cool and seldom rise above 80 degrees. Lakes freeze by late October, and the smaller ones are ice-free in early May. Spring and summer bring lupin, wild roses, fireweed, blueberry, low bush cranberry, dwarf dogwood, azalea, shooting stars, Alaska cotton; cushion pink, forget-me-nots, daisies, and columbines grow at higher elevations, and the tundra has its own flowers. Lilies grow in most of the lakes.

Several dozen bald eagles winter on Kenai; goshawks and horned owls are common, as are Arctic and common loons; pintails, green-winged teal, and common and Barrow's goldeneyes are the most numerous ducks. A surprising variety of swallows, thrushes, warblers, sparrows, and so on, nest on the refuge. White-tailed ptarmigan aren't common, but willow and rock ptarmigan and spruce grouse are.

The Russians were hunting the country for sea otters long before Captain Cook appeared in the inlet named for him in 1778. The town of Kenai is the second oldest town in Alaska, and the original Russian chapel is still there, a small square wooden building with the blue onion-shaped steeple of the Orthodox Church overlooking Cook Inlet.

Kenai is a good example of a multiple-use refuge. Its campgrounds, canoe routes, fishing and hunting contribute to the recreation of Alaskans and many visitors. About 143,000 people visited Kenai in 1965, and the number of visitors has been increasing since then. Some 1,200 moose were shot on the refuge in 1965, and a vast number of fish were caught. The refuge contributes significantly to the Alaskan economy; it has timber and fur resources for controlled cutting and trapping; it protects streams where millions of salmon spawn; and 30,000 barrels of oil are taken out of part of the refuge lands a day. Former Secretary of the Interior Douglas MacKay opened up a part of the refuge to oil companies, and while oil exploration, drilling, operation, and pipelines leave their scars on a country, the scars are being healed over under the direction of the refuge staff.

Multiple use, which helps the local economy and increases recreational opportunity, is a fine thing, but the refuge must maintain prime habitat for wildlife, clean streams, and

*The hoary marmot, a rock chuck, is related to the woodchuck of eastern United States. It lives throughout Alaska and British Columbia and sometimes crosses the northern borders of Washington, Idaho, and Montana.*

fine scenic values. Without protection they would disappear, as history has amply demonstrated, and in order to be sure of this protection the Bureau would like to have about a third of the refuge put into the National Wilderness Preservation System, which would place it beyond any possibility of being disturbed in the future. A proposal to this end has been drawn up; it is sound and forward-looking, fair to everyone, and its acceptance would guarantee some wilderness for the future. Though it would cost about two and a half million dollars above the present refuge budget, it would be worth it.

Kodiak Island, which all big-game hunters know as the typical home of the Alaskan brown bear—one of the largest carnivorous animals on earth—is a rugged and surprisingly green island with an area of about 3,500 square miles. It is in the Gulf of Alaska, and unlike most of the state has a comparatively mild climate. The winters seldom get down to zero; an average snowfall of forty-five inches, along with sixty inches of rain, keep it verdant with a flourishing cover of grass, thick brush, cottonwood, willow and alder trees, and a variety of flowering plants and berries. The mountains rise to around four thousand feet, and some of them hold snow on their summits all summer; there are many lakes and clear streams up which great numbers of red salmon ascend in the summer to spawn. The weather is often stormy, with misty, soft rain and low clouds that mask off the mountaintops. In the center of the island are great wide valleys; two-thirds up the mountains, the trees and brush fall away to leave grassy slopes, and the southern part of the island is rolling tundra.

The Kodiak National Wildlife Refuge was established in 1941 to preserve ideal habitat for the brown bears; and while headquarters is in the town of Kodiak, the center of operations is about a hundred miles away, on Karluk Lake, for when the salmon are running from the lake up the many streams that empty into it the bears gather along the streams for the fishing. It is often possible to see fifty of them in a square mile when the salmon run is on.

There are no roads on the refuge; people get around on foot or by boat, and travel into the refuge is mostly by aircraft.

Brown bears are very impressive creatures. Mature males may grow to a weight of fifteen hundred pounds and a length of thirteen feet, although their average length is ten feet; when a big male stands erect he will tower high enough above a man to make him feel quite insignificant. I was within fifteen yards of a huge golden-brown male in a grassy opening, and he didn't have to stand erect to impress me; I was perfectly happy to watch him go off on all fours after he'd looked me over.

The original range of these bears was along the coast of the Alaskan Peninsula to British Columbia, from the mountaintops to the beaches, but hunting has diminished their numbers and their range. The high-powered rifle has changed their original notion that they were the lords of creation, and even after the rifle's advent they killed many people. Now, although there is an occasional accident, they prefer to let people alone, and avoid them.

They den up for the winter high on the ridges, in shallow caves or in the lee of big rocks. Most of them are snoring away by the end of November, although some of the big males will emerge in December, wander around for a time in the snow, and den up again. April brings them out; females with cubs, which are born in January and at birth are about the size of gray squirrels, are the last to appear, toward the end of May. They must eat grass, roots, and dead fish and seals along the beaches until berries begin to ripen, and then the salmon begin to run up the streams. By early July there are usually plenty of salmon, and the bears move up and down the streams catching them, and fill up with thirty to thirty-five big salmon a day apiece. Cubs let their mothers do the fishing, and caper about on the banks, squalling for food. When the salmon run is over, quantities of berries are ripe, and the bears scatter to harvest them. The cubs, usually two or three in number, stay with their mothers during the second year.

The Kodiak Refuge produces the world's largest bears, and because hunting pressure has been increasing for the last twenty years studies are being made to learn more about them, how best to manage them, and how many of them can be shot to keep them in balance with their range. To do this, it is necessary to trap them. Anywhere from thirty- to fifty-odd bears are trapped annually.

Bears move along the lake edge or make trails through the brush along streams, and traps are set in these places. Each trap has about eight feet of chain attached to a drag in the shape of an anchor, which finally entangles itself in the brush as the bear moves about with the trap. The traps have offset jaws, to limit leg or foot injury. When a bear is caught and goes off, the trapper follows it up and tranquilizes it with a dart from a gas-operated gun if it has too much free play on the chain. It is then tied up, and another tranquilizer, lasting about an hour, is injected from a syringe at the end of a twenty-foot aluminum pole. If the bear is tightly tangled, only the second injection is used.

The ropes are taken off and the bear is examined, weighed, and measured; a dental impression is taken, and one of its incisors is pulled out to determine its age, for each year adds a ring to the tooth under the gumline. A numbered disk is put in its ear, to identify it if it is shot or trapped again. Radio tracking devices are in contemplation, so the bear's movements may be followed. It won't be long before a bear will have a hard time keeping any secrets.

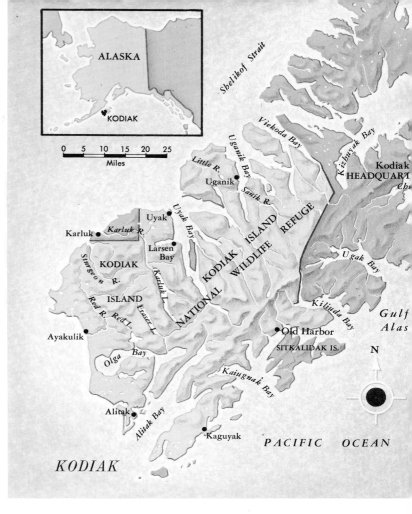

*The bald eagle gets its name from the white feathers on its head, giving it a bald look from a distance. These large eagles are becoming increasingly scarce because hunters continue to shoot them.*

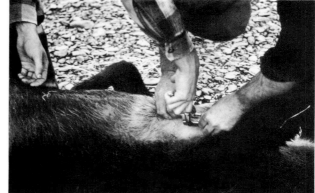

TOP: *After a bear has been caught in a trap, a refuge worker, using a syringe attached to a long pole, injects into the bear a muscle-relaxing drug.* LEFT ABOVE: *The worker approaches the bear and makes a second injection to keep the bear asleep for about an hour.* LEFT: *The bear is weighed, and a tooth is extracted to determine its age.* ABOVE: *The old method of tattooing the bear with an identification number, shown here, has been replaced with a system of placing a tag in the ear. Thus identified, the bear is released.*

RIGHT: *Among the most colorful of seabirds on the Alaskan refuges is the horned puffin.*

In the eight years or so that this has been going on, no one has been killed or even hurt. Perhaps this is partly good luck and partly good management, but it's not the world's most uneventful business.

Richard Hensel is the manager now, and Will Troyer was a former manager; they worked together frequently. They told me of several incidents. One concerned a big bear entangled in such thick brush that they couldn't get a shot at it with the dart gun, so Hensel climbed a tree near the bear, carrying the gun, until he reached a crotch that gave him a clear view. Troyer, who was on the ground, tossed a rock into the thicket to make the bear move; the rock hit it on the head, and added to its displeasure. It was roaring and thrashing about, and Hensel was getting ready to shoot at it, when the tree cracked and he and the crotch began a slow descent toward the raging bear. The crotch paused in its descent a little above the bear's reach; and Hensel, deciding to leave before the crotch began to drop again, made a mighty leap, turned in the air, and landed running. He thinks he might have established a speed record. At another time, Troyer was out alone following a trapped bear, and caught up with it in such a thick place that he couldn't see it. He climbed a tree and discovered that he was in the tree holding the drag. The bear, at the end of the stretched chain, discovered him at about the same time, and moved under the tree to pull it down. There was another tree about eight feet away; Troyer reached it in a single wild jump and so got out of the bear's reach.

Being out alone on a trapline isn't recommended; usually there are four or five people and a lot of gear, such as ropes, syringes, scales, and whatnot. One man carries a rifle and another a repeating shotgun loaded with buckshot and several small devices like grenades called "shellcrackers" that explode with a burst of flame and a roar. These are usually used on mother bears whose cub has put a foot in a trap, for these mothers may sometimes charge. It is usually evident at a distance that a cub has been caught because of its bawling, and the trappers make plenty of noise as they approach to give the mother time for second thoughts. Sometimes she goes off and isn't seen, but sometimes she remains and makes a nuisance of herself. A shell-cracker or two detonated over her head or near her will usually make her go away. A few of them have required considerable harassment, and in any event everyone is prepared to run. If the worst comes to the worst, there is always the rifle. They haven't had to shoot a bear yet; no one knows whether the rifle would stop one at such close range, but they think it would, and go cheerily about their work.

One hundred and sixteen species of birds have been recorded on Kodiak, and many of them stay the winter. Among them are loons, a quarter of a million ducks of six species, kingfishers, ravens, dippers, winter wrens, black-capped chickadees and various thrushes, pine grosbeaks, pine siskins, white-winged crossbills, fox and song sparrows, and snow buntings. There are many rock and willow ptarmigan. Sometimes emperor geese will appear, and Canada geese, black brant, snow and white-fronted geese move through. Bald eagles are quite abundant and almost always within view; 150 to 200 pairs nest on the island.

The assistant refuge manager (a wonderful camp cook) showed me the refuge from the air. We saw many bears fishing in the creeks, wandering along the shoreline, or on the mountainsides. They all paused in their affairs to keep an eye on the low-flying plane, and one big male in a stream stood up and swung at us with a forepaw. A female with two cubs halfway up a mountainside spanked the cubs along toward a thicket and cover when they tried to sit down and watch us. On the southern shore, a herd of seals took wildly to the water as we flew over them. The wide interior valleys were full of meandering streams and potholes; salmon were lying in dark congregations off the mouths of the creeks. Aside from a few salmon canneries along the bays near the sea, several small native villages on the coast, and two campgrounds the Bureau has put in, the refuge has been left pretty much as men found it.

The first white settlement in Alaska was established by the Russians at Three Saints Bay, near the present town of Kodiak. There was trouble for some time with the natives, a race called Koniags, which numbered about six thousand. They were a tall, healthy, tough, copper-colored people; the men were darker than the women because of their habit of boating naked. They lived in houses that were half underground, roofed with whale ribs,

*The snowshoe rabbit, or varying hare, is perfectly camouflaged in both its brown summer coat and its white winter one.*

skins, and earth, and spent a good deal of the time steaming themselves in a sauna, after which they would plunge naked into the cold ocean. They were painted and tattooed, and some sewed designs on their skins. Their villages were usually built near mud flats that were exposed at low tide, where they could dig for clams and mussels, and they made angled stone weirs across the streams to catch salmon; remains of some of these weirs can still be seen in the Karluk River. They made out well enough until the white men came, but after that were reduced by ill treatment and white men's diseases. There are about eight hundred of them now; most of them work in salmon canneries or guide bear hunters.

The Bureau has introduced a number of animals on Kodiak. Deer, muskrats, snowshoe hares, and beaver seem to be doing well, and there are Olympic elk on Afognak Island to the north. There is a small reindeer herd on southern Kodiak. The island is too damp for Dall's sheep, but it is hoped that mountain goats will do well. Mink and marten have been brought in, and sea otters are returning to the northern coast.

Kodiak has no snakes, lizards, or frogs, and only two poisonous plants; there are few troublesome insects. Flowers such as lupins, forget-me-nots, shooting stars, violets, orchids, daisies, wild geraniums, and iris bloom through spring and summer; pink fireweed grows in large stands in grassy openings and glows red in the fall when the leaves turn. In some places, it is still possible to find ash from Katmai Volcano on Unimak Island, eighty miles to the north, which erupted violently in 1912 and scattered ash and fragmented rock over a wide area. Two to three feet fell in the town of Kodiak, and the town was temporarily evacuated. An earthquake several years ago brought in a great tidal wave that knocked down many buildings, which have since been rebuilt.

67

The Nunivak Island National Wildlife Refuge covers 1,109,400 acres of Nunivak Island in the Bering Sea, and is populated mostly by Eskimos. It is about forty miles offshore, an old volcanic island now covered with tundra on which the old craters have been worn down by weather and time. The highest peak is 1,675 feet high; most of the peaks are green and gently sloping, and several of the craters hold lakes. The island in the main is fairly flat or gently rolling, with high bluffs behind the beaches, and there are many streams and tundra ponds. The sea cliffs on the western side hold vast sea-bird rookeries, and are usually fogged in. The weather on Nunivak is usually bad, as it is in most places around the Bering Sea. On the rare clear days, the grassy slopes of the mountains and the tundra are a lovely green, and the sea is one of the most beautiful blues in the world.

The only musk oxen in our country are on Nunivak, and are the descendants of a small herd brought in from Greenland in 1930. Our native musk oxen were exterminated by the middle of the last century, and these few animals were brought in to furnish a nucleus from which our ranges could be repopulated. There are about six hundred of them now, enough to begin the restocking of other places.

The musk ox is an odd creature, a little like the buffalo in its anatomy, with an undercoat of dense wool as fine as cashmere and an outercoat of long black hair that reaches nearly to the ground. A big bull will be eight feet or so long, stand five feet high at the shoulders, and weigh around seven hundred pounds. It has a small gland below each eye which secretes a musky odor, and horns that cover the forehead in a wide boss, curve down past the eyes, and recurve upward again. Unlike other Arctic animals, the musk ox doesn't migrate. Its warm coat protects it from any weather, and it roots down through the snow for grass and dwarf-willow browse.

Musk oxen move swiftly and nimbly, but their habit of lining up to face wolves and bears brought them to disaster against men. Several dogs could bring them to a halt, and then men would stand off and shoot them all. Old bulls always stand between their families and danger, and they have never learned to change their defense.

An annual count of musk oxen is made from the air, and I was fortunate enough to go along with Dave Spencer, the supervisor of Alaskan refuges, when he made the count in July. After packing our sleeping bags and emergency rations, we took off across Cook Inlet and flew through the Alaska Range by several river valleys to the headwaters of the Kuskokwim River and Bethel; the peaks stood jagged and snow-capped around us. Presently, we were through the mountains, and the coastal plain full of tundra ponds and winding rivers was below us; finally we landed at Bethel, lonely on the tundra and inhabited mostly by Eskimos, and spent the night with the manager of the Nunivak and Clarence Rhode refuges.

The next morning we took off again. The

*A large female, or sow,*
*big brown bear wades across Canyon Creek on*
*the Kodiak National Wildlife Refuge.*

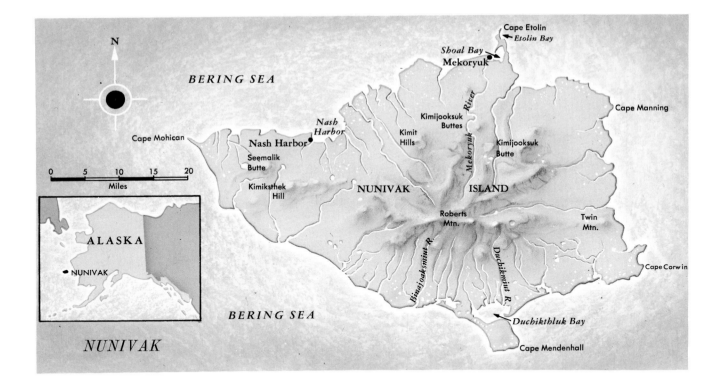

tundra was more than half water now, and stretched away as far as the eye could see, without a sign of man. Over an hour later, we came to the coast. There were low clouds over the leaden sea, and great gray mud flats stretched along the shore. There was a dead walrus there, surrounded by gulls, from which some wandering Eskimo had hacked the tusks; families of emperor geese and sandhill cranes moved about. We gained altitude, and flying through the gauzy overcast headed for Nunivak.

Finally, it began to take fragmentary shape, a big dark island patched with snow, the low hills rising between fingers of cloud. We dropped down again, swung inland, and began to scan the country, and finally found our first musk oxen along a streambed—a bull, four cows, and three calves. As we banked steeply around them, they ran together and lined up, the calves under their mothers. The bull, larger and paler than the others, with a rounded hump on his shoulders,

charged out and spun like a top, tossing his head to hook us and pawing dust; you could almost hear him snorting defiance.

We marked their number and location on the map, and flew on to begin our transects of the island, concentrating on our search, for it is easy to miss a few tiny dots lost on the great sweep of the tundra, masked by a hill, or out of sight in the bend of a stream. We recorded a number of musk oxen during the rest of the day, flew over several Eskimo families camped along the streams to catch and dry salmon, and landed late in the afternoon to set up our quarters in a Quonset hut in the Eskimo village of Mekoryuk. The village is a fairly large one, most of it strung along the bluff overlooking the water. Homemade, enclosed sleds driven by small second-hand airplane engines sit about, waiting for winter and the fox trapping, and there are a number of boats alongshore. There are usually a few wolfish dogs tied here and there, but their number has greatly declined now that the mechanized age is here. Eskimo children with spinning rods fish off the beach in the evenings.

We flew transects for several days, gradually covering the island and adding to our count. On our last afternoon we found a herd on a sloping peak about seven hundred feet high, and as it was within a mile or so of a big tundra pond Dave decided to land and see how close we could get to the herd on foot. We landed, tied the plane to a dwarf willow, and started across the tundra. It was full of grassy hummocks about thirty inches high, and we dodged an erratic and wandering course between them. The tundra was full of low flowers—ledum, green Arctic gentian, woolly lousewort, wild rose, crowberry, cranberry, and many others—in an astonishing variety and range of colors. Small birds popped in and out of the hummocks, and we flushed several ptarmigan.

Finally, we came to rising ground and short grass starred with flowers, and rocks bright with lichens. We climbed the mountainside. Up near the crest, we could see the backs of the musk oxen, and used the contour of the ground to keep them from seeing us. Finally, we came over a shoulder and found the herd about two hundred yards away—a humped old bull and a yearling, six cows, and three calves, dark against the green hillside and the gray sky. They didn't see us at first, and Dave began to move closer. Having watched the bulls from the air, I wondered if they would be inclined to charge us, but Dave didn't seem concerned and continued to walk. The bull lifted his head and stared at us, and

*When danger threatens musk oxen, the bulls form a first line of defense while the young stay close to their mothers.*

*The reindeer is a domesticated Old World caribou.*
*Like the caribou, reindeer are unique members of the deer family*
*because the females grow antlers. There are*
*probably about 12,000 reindeer on Nunivak.*

then the cows looked up. Suddenly they all whirled about and galloped swiftly out of sight around the mountain.

We moved on to see if we could get closer to them again, and presently were just below the crest, and carefully raised our heads. Our little herd had joined a much larger one that we hadn't seen from the air, and now there were about forty-five of them. They were well bunched, backed by the long, sweeping miles of tundra spotted with lakes and patched with snow. They saw us and faced us, with the bulls a little in front. They all ran again, but not very far. We dropped down and crawled

around a height of ground, and this time came out so close to them that I could have thrown a rock and hit them. They faced us again, cattle from the Pleistocene Age that might at one time have wandered as far south as Pennsylvania, not sure what we were, and more curious than hostile. The calves ran under their mothers, and the bulls moved out a little more. We all stared at one another for a long moment, and then one of them snorted, and all, except the largest bull, whirled and galloped off down the long slope of the mountain. The old bull stood firm for a short time in case there should be pursuit, and then gal-

*In the rugged and majestic Alaska Range,*
*glacier-fed streams flow through steep-sided*
*valleys gouged out by ice.*

loped after them. His long coat swung from side to side, like the ground-sweeping skirts of a dancer. They didn't stop again, and finally vanished over the crest of a distant crater.

It had been a great pleasure and a privilege to see and be so close to them; probably not a hundred men now living had enjoyed that privilege.

Dave decided that we would fly back through Merrill Pass, probably the most dangerous pass in Alaska, if the weather was good. We checked with the FAA in Bethel, and found that it would be. We took off and headed for the Alaska Range, higher and more rugged here than in the country we had flown over coming out.

Presently foothills took the place of the watery flat plain; then peaks began to rise. They grew higher and closer to us, and the green of the lower elevations fell away and gave place to bare rock and snow. The country continued to climb, and we climbed with it; it kept closing in and there were more bare rock and snow. Clouds and icefields ringed us in, summits sawed at the sky, and great seamed mountainsides plunged down. Now and then there would be lakes at the ends of the valleys, lonely, blue, and beautiful; probably no one had walked around their margins for years. A vast valley opened up in the sea of peaks, and we turned into it, but before we had gone very far we turned again, still climbing, into a side valley that seemed scarcely wide enough for the plane. Far below, at the narrow stony entrance to our valley, was a crumpled DC-3, but I never heard its story and didn't think about it then, for that passage was like a narrow misty valley between skyscrapers, its rocky walls seeming only a few feet beyond the wing tips. Still we climbed, and it should have been a terrifying place, but it was so wildly beautiful that it brought a feeling of exultation.

Ahead was a great rounded dome between the walls, and we passed over it; on the other side the world fell away and opened out into a great lake. We were through the pass.

The land dropped slowly down to spruces, winding rivers, and muskeg again; the wild and lovely range withdrew to either side. We came above Cook Inlet, and found that the white whales were following the salmon run to the north. There were hundreds of them, very tiny and white against the dark water from our altitude of 3,500 feet, each appearing for a moment on the surface to blow and then diving again, pale, dissolving blurs finally vanishing into the depths. It was fine to encounter these creatures of the sea, for they are as much a part of the great northern land as the musk ox; to see them by chance in the cold dark water filled out the trip to Nunivak, and somehow made it complete.

# The Southwest

Although the Central Flyway shares some of its birds with the Pacific Flyway, most of them travel through Region Two, which includes Wyoming, Utah, Arizona, Colorado, New Mexico, Kansas, Oklahoma, and Texas. The region is administered from Albuquerque, New Mexico. It contains prairie, mountain, and desert country, and has a great variety of habitat and wildlife. It includes five big-game ranges, among them the National Elk Refuge at Jackson Hole, Wyoming, near the spectacular Grand Teton Range, and the Fish Springs Refuge in Utah, a green oasis in the Salt Lake Desert. Wichita Mountains and Aransas Refuges are now described.

*A lanky jack rabbit escapes the heat of the midday sun under a mesquite on the Desert National Wildlife Range, Nevada.*

The Aransas National Wildlife Refuge is about seventy-five miles north of Corpus Christi, Texas, near Austwell, on the wide, flat coastal plain. It is surrounded on three sides by water, the bays that lie behind the barrier islands on the Gulf of Mexico. The Intracoastal Waterway bounds it to the east, and from a boat on the waterway families of whooping cranes, the last of their kind on earth, can frequently be seen feeding during the winter months. They can't be approached closer than a half mile on land, but are much less wary of moving boats. The day I went down the waterway in the refuge launch with the manager, we were within a hundred yards of a pair and their rusty-colored young one. It was an exciting thing to be so close to birds that are so rare and have aroused so much interest.

Tall and stately in their gleaming white plumage, with red patches of bare skin on their crowns, these great birds have brought people to the refuge from all over the world, and newspapers throughout the country note their arrival in the fall from their nesting grounds near the Arctic Circle and their departure in the spring.

It has been estimated that there were about five thousand whoopers once, which nested over a wide northern area and wintered in the various marshes from Mexico to Utah and South Carolina; the only wild ones left nest near Great Slave Lake in Northwest Territories of Canada, and winter at Aransas. They love wild country and require large territories, and through the years have been shot and crowded out by the white man's march across the land. In the autumn of 1941,

there were only fifteen cranes at Aransas, and it was feared they were about to vanish forever. Then they began to increase, but the increase wasn't constant. The population rose and fell again, but by the fall of 1967 there were thirty-nine adults and nine young at Aransas. No one is very happy about the situation yet, for the population is too concentrated, and a stretch of bad weather or some other condition might still wipe them all out. We have an arrangement with the Canadian Government now to take a few eggs annually and hatch them at Patuxent to have a reserve. It is hoped that these birds will establish new territories and not migrate so far, but no one knows yet how this will work out. Efforts to raise young cranes in captivity haven't been completely successful, and migration time is very dangerous for the cranes, for hunters still shoot them.

Because the cranes are so easily disturbed by people and could be frightened off the refuge by them, visitors aren't allowed near the marsh where they feed, but can watch them from a tower with binoculars. Fenced food patches have been planted in the interior of the refuge, to keep them away from the waterway where they can't be guarded all the time, and studies are constantly being made to find out what foods they like best and whether pesticides are affecting them. Strangely enough, the whoopers, which chase other whoopers off their mile-square territories in the marsh, lose their belligerence in the food patches and feed together.

They are so tall and gleaming white that they can be seen for a great distance, and

*The roseate spoonbill inhabits both shallow coastal waters and freshwater ponds inland.*

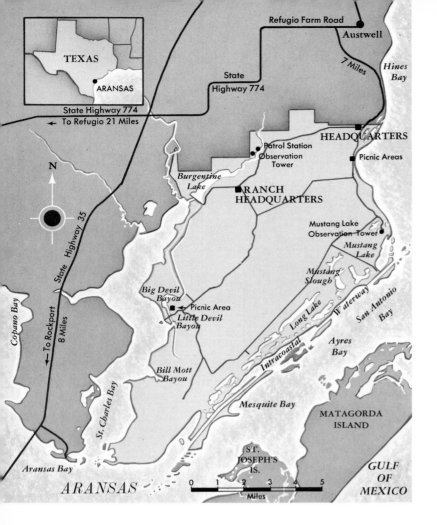

*The collared peccary is North America's only native wild pig. It lives in the United States only in southeastern Arizona, southern New Mexico, and southern Texas.*

evoke a special emotion. Flying with their long necks and legs extended, their seven-foot wings so white that the black wing tips make a dramatic contrast, they call to mind a time when our country was uncrowded and they flew across it so high as to be unseen but known by their resonant, ringing calls coming out of the sky.

They are strong and graceful flyers, fond of soaring a mile or so in the air. Early observers reported that they liked to engage in aerial games and complicated evolutions, dancing in the air to their own music, and descending in wild dives to within fifty feet of the ground, and their stately mating dances on the ground were famous. They were a part of wild America, and our lives are poorer for their lack. We can only hope that the things that are being done will bring them back and that we will know them again over a wider area.

There is more to Aransas than whooping cranes and the strip of flatland that holds them; the 47,000 acres of the refuge are different from the flat farmland that surrounds it, and is divided between brackish marsh, grassland, woods, and live-oak and blackjack-oak thickets and fresh-water impoundments, as well as fifty-five miles of tidal flats and shallow bays along its shoreline. Probably a thousand sandhill cranes, smaller than whoopers and once on the edge of extinction, winter on the refuge, and almost three hundred species of other birds have been seen there. Birds like the pauraque, road runner, white-tailed hawk, pyrrhuloxia, and caracara —all near the northern limit of their range— are novelties for the northern bird watcher, and there are roseate spoonbills (once almost exterminated by plume hunters), white ibis, egrets, herons, and black-necked stilts.

Most of the refuge is low upland, with a great deal of brush that is thorny and almost impenetrable by man, and so full of life that Bureau personnel love to visit. Winter is mild there, and the acorn crops sustain an almost unbelievable number of deer as well as fox squirrels, wild turkeys, and the javelina, or collared peccary, our only wild pig. These creatures moved about in groups and combined against their enemies, and there are many old tales about them treeing people who stirred them up. Once they were very numerous, but their hides came to have commercial value and they were hunted down. They are wary now, but can often be seen at Aransas as they move out of cover in the early mornings or late afternoons. Apparently, they like to sleep in hollow logs or small caves, and the last one backs in and faces outward as a sentinel.

Harder to find are the big wild boars from the Prussian forests, imported before 1937 when the refuge was still the St. Francis Ranch. These redoubtable creatures are large, very strong, and have long and dangerous tusks. Unfortunately, they are very destructive, and the refuge personnel are attempting to eliminate them. Because of this they are very wary. About 350 of them are shot every year, but it will be a long time before they are

*When the whooping cranes arrive at Aransas, each pair of birds with its young establishes a territory and defends it against other cranes. Here a big male crane drives out an intruder.*

*The opossum usually has a litter of from eight to eighteen,*
*but only about seven survive the period in their mother's pouch.*
*When the young leave the pouch, the mother*
*carries them around on her back.*

done away with. From the time of ancient Greece until the invention of gunpowder, these animals were hunted with hounds, and it took a lot of courage to dare one of them in cover with a spear, for they are shifty and powerful and could be upon a man in a twinkling, and rip him up.

Blacktail jack rabbits and cottontails live on the refuge, and numerous raccoons, opossums, striped skunks, Plains pocket gophers, red wolves, and the largest coyotes in North America. Gray foxes are on the increase, and sometimes a badger appears, al-

though Aransas is somewhat east of its usual range. Two other animals that have been seen only once or twice are the bassaris (sometimes called cacomistle, or ring-tailed cat) and the coati. They both belong to the raccoon family, and are as active and inquisitive as their ring-tailed cousin. The bassaris, of a rich orange-brown color with a brown- and white-striped tail, almost as long as its fifteen-inch body, and dark spectacles, is strictly nocturnal and so shy and elusive that it is very seldom seen. The coati measures about fifty-five inches, of which the tail takes up about half. On its usual range, south of Texas, it marches about in troops with its long tail sticking straight up in the air. It is more arboreal than the bassaris.

Bobcats are fairly common at Aransas, but are largely nocturnal; the ocelot, the pretty, inoffensive spotted cat about the size of a lynx, was once fairly common but has probably disappeared. The armadillo, a curious, armor-plated little creature, is occasionally encountered. It was once confined to southern Texas but is spreading northward, and in some mysterious way has even managed to get itself across the Mississippi. It is easy to approach and a great temptation to small boys for that reason, but it shouldn't be captured; it dies very quickly in captivity.

Old-timers say that the Blackjack Peninsula, which is now the refuge, was once a great plain of grass and was used to pasture cattle. Rockport, the nearest town, was a great shipping point for cattle before the era of trail herds began. As in so many places, the peninsula was overgrazed, and brush took over. The refuge people would like to clear the entire southern end of the peninsula, plant more grass, and put in additional ponds that would support more waterfowl. They would also like to bring back Attwater's prairie chicken, which threatens to disappear because of the brush.

If this were done, there would still be plenty of room for the animals that prefer the brush. It wouldn't interfere with tourist travel either, for it is roadless now. A good deal of the refuge is, because of its function, but the visitor needn't feel slighted; there are enough roads now to give him a fine sample of the place.

*Bobcats are seldom about during the day, but at nightfall, they hunt for rabbits and hares, often covering twenty-five miles in a night.* **In winter, bobcats sometimes kill deer.**

Southwestern Oklahoma rolls a little but is largely prairie. It has mild winters, and is mostly farming and grazing country, and our native grasses—the bluestems, Indian grass, and buffalo grass—which supported vast herds of game that attracted Comanches, Wichitas, and Kiowas, has largely disappeared before the plow. It was opened to settlement in 1901, and many of the estimated 10,000,000 longhorn cattle that were driven northward out of Texas went through it. Its lush and nourishing grasses impressed the cattlemen, and contributed to the settlement of the country.

The longhorns, which were introduced into Mexico in 1521 and were spread over the Southwest by Francisco Vázquez de Coronado and other Spanish explorers, had their day and began to disappear around the turn of the century before cattle that were easier to handle and produced more beef in a shorter time. They went the way of the native grasses and the deer, the great herds of buffalo and elk and pronghorn, and left the cowboy who had struggled with them to become a legendary figure that is peculiarly American and is known all over the world.

The Wichita Mountains Northwest Refuge is in this country, in the middle of the old, eroded Wichita Mountains that rise from the plain. It has great meadows and wide valleys, post-oak and blackjack-oak woods, and wooded stream bottoms. The big meadows, once so badly overgrazed, have been managed so well that the native grasses have come back, and the buffalo, elk, and longhorn have been brought back with them. Wichita is one of the very few places left that shows what

the old West was like, how it looked before the white man changed it, and a million people or more come to see it every year.

The refuge, which covers 59,020 acres, was made a game sanctuary by President Theodore Roosevelt in 1905. By that time the buffalo that had darkened the Plains were gone, and Oklahoma's elk, pronghorn, and wild turkey had vanished with them; there were only a few deer left in remote corners of the country. The deer began to increase again under protection, and in 1907 six buffalo bulls and nine cows were brought in from the New York Zoo. They made a train journey of over 1,800 miles to get back to the country which had once known millions of their race, and the few Indians present when they were released watched with tears streaming down their faces.

The Wichita herd now has twice as many buffalo in it as there once remained in the United States in wild and captive herds combined, and many of them can be seen along the roads of the refuge. A bull buffalo in his prime is a magnificent and redoubtable beast, standing six feet high at the shoulder, with a length of nine feet or more and a weight of a ton or so. His massive head, which is carried low, and his humped shoulders make him look somewhat clumsy, but he isn't clumsy in the least. A buffalo surprised lying down doesn't get up in installments like a cow, but bounces up in one motion with astonishing quickness, and is under way. This capacity for swift action is made more dangerous by the buffalo's great strength; there is a record of one bull that charged a cow pony, im-

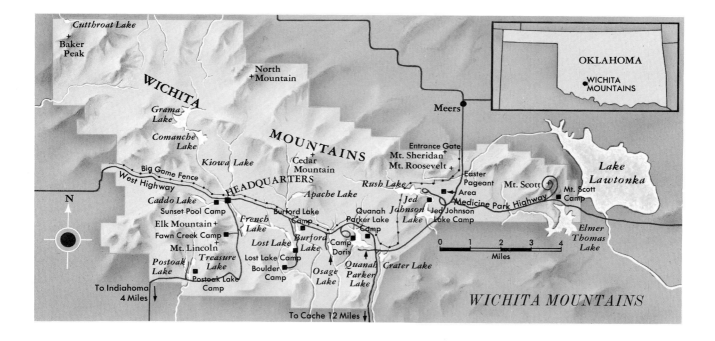

Map labels: Cutthroat Lake, Baker Peak, WICHITA, North Mountain, OKLAHOMA, WICHITA MOUNTAINS, Grama Lake, Comanche Lake, MOUNTAINS, Meers, Kiowa Lake, Cedar Mountain, Big Game Fence, West Highway, HEADQUARTERS, Apache Lake, Rush Lake, Entrance Gate, Mt. Sheridan, Mt. Roosevelt, Easter Pageant Area, Mt. Scott, Lake Lawtonka, Caddo Lake, Sunset Pool Camp, Elk Mountain, French Lake, Burford Lake Camp, Jed Johnson, Quanah Parker Lake Camp, Jed Johnson Lake, Jed Johnson Lake Camp, Medicine Park Highway, Mt. Scott Camp, Fawn Creek Camp, Mt. Lincoln, Lost Lake, Burford Lake, Camp Doris, Postoak Lake, Treasure Lake, Lost Lake Camp, Boulder Camp, Osage Lake, Quanah Parker Lake, Crater Lake, Elmer Thomas Lake, Postoak Lake Camp, To Indiahoma 4 Miles, To Cache 12 Miles, Miles, WICHITA MOUNTAINS, N

paled it, lifted it off the ground, and carried the pony and its rider for a hundred yards at a dead run before pausing to kill the pony.

The buffalo at Wichita are usually seen in small groups, for they seem to prefer it that way; old bulls are kept in pastures away from the roads, for age makes them morose and dangerous. Buffalo always were, and still are, chancy animals to approach, and many settlers who tried to domesticate them were killed or had narrow escapes from death. Buffalo probably killed more people than all other American animals put together. There haven't been any dramatic incidents of this sort at Wichita, where visitors are warned to stay in their cars when buffalo or longhorns are nearby, although several visitors who have ignored this warning have been slightly injured.

The buffalo's story is told earlier in this book, but to see them at Wichita brings to a focus a mental picture that typifies more than any other the early history of the vast, midcontinent sea of grass that was the Great Plains. Buffalo moved across them in incredible numbers; they were the staff of life for the Indians and the early trappers and explorers, the trailmakers whose trails the railroads followed, animals whose destruction preoccupied an army of men for a decade or more and turned the tide toward conservation of our wildlife. All this is in the loose group of big dark animals crossing the road before you or resting in the grass.

There are about three hundred longhorns on the refuge, and the herd is kept to that number. By 1927, when it was decided to establish a herd at Wichita, longhorns had become so scarce that two Forest Service men had to travel five thousand miles and look over thirty thousand cattle before they found twenty cows and three bulls that were representative.

The longhorn is a big-boned, rangy animal, rather slab-sided, long-legged, and usually sway-backed; in the old days nobody pampered it; it was left to shift for itself, and could endure heat, cold, insects, thirst, and the

*The burrowing owl is among the animals that share the prairie dog's burrow system.*

*The green plains of the Wichita Mountains Refuge protect a major herd of buffalo.*

other difficulties of life far better than any breed of cattle evolved since. It was an extraordinarily durable beast; it could climb anywhere, run like a deer, swim great distances, and march forever, but it wasn't a good commercial beef animal because it took too long to mature.

It was often said that it ran chiefly to legs and horns, and certainly the horns were notable. Five-foot spreads weren't unusual, and steers grew the most notable ones. Most of the horns curve; straight sets have probably been steamed and straightened, to stretch them. When the railroads got to Texas and steers were hauled north, many of them couldn't get through a freight-car door; the horns had to be chopped off or the steer's head twisted. Horns were made into furniture, fences, road markers, powder horns, spoons, clothes racks, and whatnot; they were an item of decoration in banks, bars, homes, and business offices. They symbolized a way of life in cattle country that is past and gone.

Being in effect a wild animal, the longhorn's continued existence was a matter of the survival of the fittest. Nobody fed, sheltered, or doctored it, and the natives handled it roughly and thought it was better off dead if it couldn't shift for itself. Cows would fight anything to protect their calves, and bulls would fight anything—including grizzly bears —for the pure joy of fighting. They protected themselves from wolves as well, or better, than the buffalo, and like the buffalo bounced to their feet in an instant, and when a bedded herd jumped up and stampeded it was a unanimous affair and seemed to happen in the twinkling of an eye.

Stampedes were one of the most dramatic things that happened in the old West, and could practically always be counted on in trail herds of longhorns, for they were wild and suspicious, and practically anything could set them off. They stampeded more often at night

*The prairie dog that once existed in the millions across the grasslands has declined in the face of agricultural expansion. Their extensive colonies, or towns, left the prarie unfit for any other use.*

than by day, and there was always a man on night watch, singing long, mournful songs to soothe them, and all hands had sure-footed night horses picketed close by to mount when the sudden roar of a stampede brought them out of their blankets. Galloping through the blackness, often in pouring rain and wild lightning, with static electricity running along the long, tossing horns and any metal worn by the cowboy or his horse, the cowboys would try to turn the leaders and "throw them into a mill"—push them into a circle that would wind up upon itself. This was always a desperate enterprise, done at full speed; and if the cowboy's horse fell or went over a bank, he was usually done for. Failing to mill the cattle, the cowboys had to round them up the next day from all over the country before the trail drive could move on.

The longhorn was the staff of life for Texas and the Southwest as much as the buffalo was the staff of life for the Indians, for there was no other industry. The animal took over the vast, unfenced sea of grass and the

*Showing cattle set on the run by a lightning bolt, this engraving,
made for Leslie's in 1881, portrays the drama of a stampede.
Anything could set the herd in motion, and losses were sometimes high.*

*The Wichita Mountains herd of longhorns shows the same color and horn
span that were characteristic of the cattle of the Old West.*

lives of the people, and when pressed ran for refuge into the *brasada,* the dense, terrible thickets where every bush bore thorns to claw the hides of men and horses.

Longhorns were driven across the deserts to California and up the Chisholm Trail to the railroad at Abilene; they filled the Plains from which the Indians and the buffalo had been extirpated; our ranching industry was founded upon their hardihood and vitality. They could survive the Texas fever that killed softer cattle, but the laws against the ticks that carried the fever brought in fencing that closed the open range; and plows that broke up the grassland followed the fencing. The days of the longhorns were done; the folk tales and legends of their wild and romantic past are all that is left.

Two hundred and sixteen species of birds have been seen at Wichita; elk and wild turkeys have been brought back, and there are coyotes, red wolves, foxes red and gray, armadillos, blacktail jack rabbits, and many other creatures. When I was there several years ago, there was a colony of black-tailed prairie dogs—creatures which once existed in billions on the Plains, and are now very hard to find. They lived in colonies in the ground and cleared half an acre around their entrances

so that enemies couldn't surprise them, but burrowing owls, weasels, and rattlesnakes overcame this difficulty by moving in and living with them. They were the favorite targets for young Indians, who worked out on them with their first bows and arrows; they supported legions of coyotes, badgers, hawks, owls, black-footed ferrets, weasels, and snakes. White men destroyed their enemies and increased their food supply with crops, and their numbers increased to such an extent that they seriously cut down grazing for cattle. War was declared on them; a long campaign of poison gas and poison bait has about wiped them out.

About half the refuge is open to the public; there are fifty miles of good roads, and many camping and picnic areas, swimming beaches, hiking trails, and stocked lakes. An Easter pageant is given every year, and Fort Sill, with a museum built around pioneer and Indian fighting days, is nearby. There are places where there are fences along the roads, but in a good deal of the refuge there are none. Looking across the native grasses, so largely vanished from the Plains, one sees the buffalo, longhorn, elk, deer, or turkey as people saw them long ago.

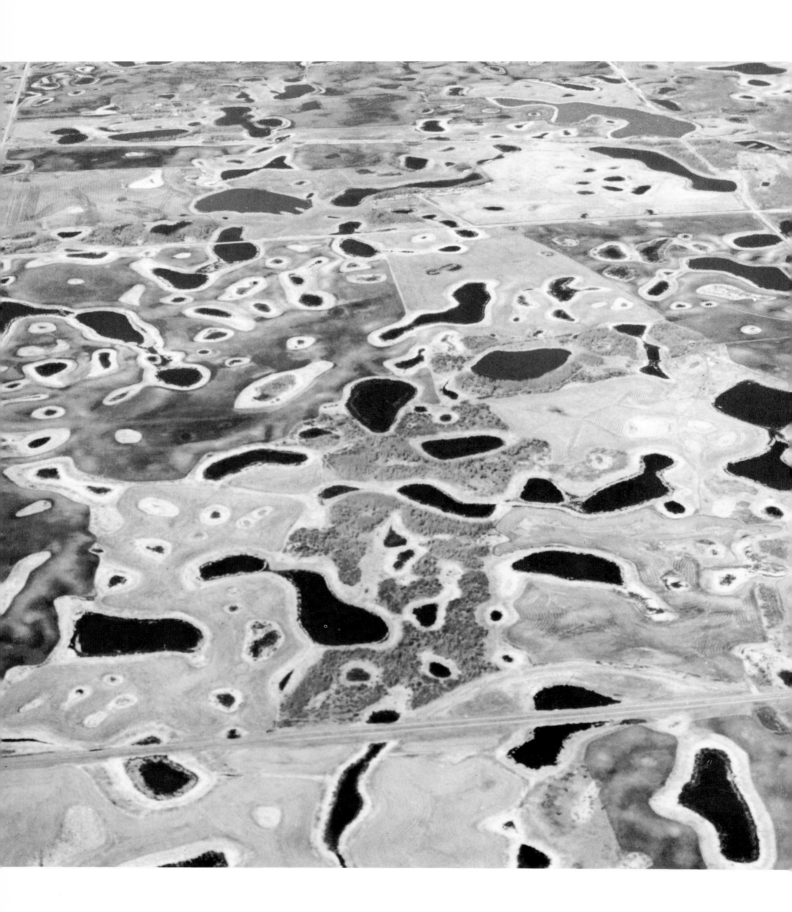

# The Midcontinent and the Pothole Country

Region Three takes in Illinois, Indiana, Iowa, Michigan, Minnesota, Missouri, Nebraska, Ohio, Wisconsin, and North and South Dakota. It is administered from Indianapolis, and runs through the center of the United States from the Canadian border, where winter temperatures drop to forty degrees below zero, to southern Missouri, which has almost subtropical weather. A good deal of it, particularly in the northern half, was originally marshland with many lakes and a vast number of small ponds called potholes, which were gouged out by the last glacier to cover that country. In years of normal rainfall these potholes catch rainwater and hold it, often to the end of summer, and millions of ducks nested and brought up their young in them. Because each pair of ducks wanted a pothole of their own, and wouldn't allow another pair of their own species in it (although they don't object to the presence of other species), a great many potholes were needed.

Around the beginning of this century, when many people went west to farm the rich soil of the prairies, settlers and real-estate operators began to drain the potholes. Thousands upon thousands of them were drained, and much of this drainage produced poor farming land because it was so low and level that it stayed wet in years of high rainfall. Also, many potholes had bottoms of decayed vegetation called "peat," which dried in years of low rainfall, caught fire, and burned out. The result was that much of this land was wasted and not good for anything. Besides this, the drainage ditches carried off rainfall too quickly; because it didn't percolate down into the underground water table, the table dropped. People had to dig deeper wells all the time, and cities couldn't get enough water. The drainage ditches carried soil away, silted up the rivers, and caused floods. In dry cycles the soil blew away and caused great dust storms that dimmed the sun as far away as Washington, D.C.

Because of unwise drainage, which produced floods and dust storms, millions of potholes were destroyed, and by 1958 waterfowl and other wetland creatures were in such trouble that Congress passed a law that embodied a program to save what wetlands were still there. This program, called the Wetlands Program, empowers the Bureau of Sport Fisheries and Wildlife to buy permanent

*Hundreds of thousands of water-filled depressions,*
*or potholes, make the northern prairie states among the most productive*
*waterfowl breeding areas in North America.*

89

marshes or, where these marshes or potholes are small, scattered, or intermittent, to pay the owner to leave them there. He may not burn, drain, or fill them up, but he keeps his other property rights and may hunt, trap, farm, or graze cattle on them. All this is paid for with money from duck stamps, which every duck hunter must buy, and arrangements are made to reimburse the counties in which these wetlands lie because taxes aren't paid on them any more.

If we want to keep our ducks, it is most important to keep the wetlands we have left, and the program is going well at this writing. A great number of ducks are hatched on the Canadian prairies, which are also being drained. The Canadian Wildlife Service now has a wetlands program of its own, however, and works closely with us.

As you drive across the great prairies you will pass a number of potholes where there are pairs of ducks, and the question will come into your mind why these ducks don't go to nearby refuges where everything possible is done to make them happy. The answer is that one pothole holds something that attracts them while another nearby is ignored. We do not know why this is, but we are trying to find out. Ducks are almost as bad as people in their individual preferences, and if you want more ducks you have to pay attention to this. When you say to a pair of ducks: "There's a lot of room in that nice safe refuge up the road a way," they don't seem to hear you. Maybe they will change their minds someday, but in the meantime you have to give them what they want, and what they want is potholes. When there are more potholes, there are more ducks, and this is what the Wetlands Program has in mind.

There are thirty-four primary refuges in Region Three, and a great number of supplementary ones under the Wetlands Program. Agassiz, J. Clark Salyer, and Lostwood are rather typical ones, and are described in the following pages.

The northwestern corner of Minnesota, where the Agassiz National Wildlife Refuge lies, is prairie, vast and level, and the eye can see for miles across it; the sweep is broken only by lines of trees, planted as a shelter belt after the Dust Bowl of the thirties, or an occasional farmhouse or grain elevator. This section is near the valley of the Red River of the North, and was once the bottom of prehistoric Lake Agassiz, which covered an area greater than that of all the Great Lakes; and when the last glacier melted, much of it was left as marsh where many great trees grew. What wasn't in marsh was covered by luxuriant short grass, and there were a multitude of potholes; the entire area was a paradise for wildlife.

The early settlers turned to market hunting for their cash crop, for there was a great profusion of rabbits, moose, ducks, geese, mink, and other creatures, and before 1900 wagonloads of game and fish were being hauled out. Much of it was drained for farming, but it wasn't farming country; it was too flat, and either dried out in drought periods or flooded after spring thaws or heavy rains. By 1915 the country and the people were in trouble: waterfowl abandoned the country; moose, bear, and mink and muskrats all but disappeared; other animals were greatly reduced; and fish were exterminated. The settlers' cash crop was gone, and the state had to take over much of the land. It was a typical ill-advised drainage project of the day.

Agassiz as it is today, with its thirteen big pools of beautiful clear blue water, marshes, cropland, and wooded islands comprising in all about 61,000 acres, is the result of dikes and water-control dams which were begun in 1937 to bring the area back to its original condition as far as possible. The wildlife that was driven out has returned in astonishing numbers, and the refuge produces from 15,000 to 20,000 young ducks a year—more than any other refuge on the Mississippi Flyway.

Highway 7 runs through a part of the refuge, and there are good gravel roads to get you into a good deal of the rest of it. Ditches run along these roads, and from them there are spacious views; there are graceful black terns, Franklin's gulls, or ducks in the air, yellow-headed or red-winged blackbirds to add color to the reeds, and sometimes a drowsy mallard drake napping on top of a roadside muskrat house. In the roadside ditches in early June you pass many drakes patrolling their territories, for their mates are nesting near them in the reeds.

The drakes of most species of ducks don't help their wives raise the children, but ruddy drakes do. Besides this eccentricity, they are amusing in their courtships. They swim around the female with their tails spread and tilted far forward, extending and drawing in their heads, slapping their bright blue bills against their inflated neck sacs, and puffing out the feathers over their eyes. They utter a variety of sounds, kick the water out behind them with both feet, stand up, press their bills against their chests, and dash about over the water. Ruddies raise two broods a year, and have the worst tempers in the duck world.

There will probably be more blue-winged teal in evidence than any other ducks, for

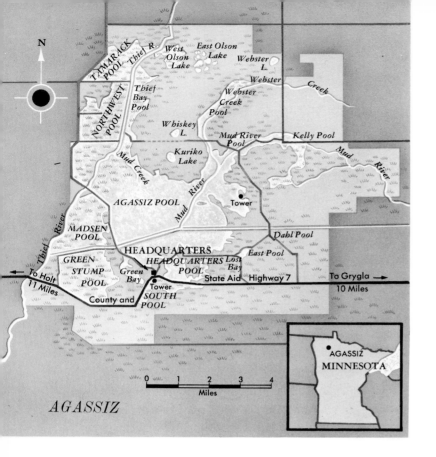

AGASSIZ

*A moose calf, unlike other members of the deer family, is not spotted at birth. It has a uniform reddish-brown color.*

they like the improved nesting conditions on the refuge. They are beautiful little birds, and migrate early; they are swift and agile flyers, and many of them fly all the way to Venezuela and Colombia to winter. There is a record of one teal that flew 4,000 miles, from the Delta Marsh in Manitoba to a lake 13,000 feet above sea level in Ecuador, and another that flew 3,800 miles in a month, an average of 125 miles a day.

There are also a lot of shovelers at Agassiz. They are boldly marked ducks with very large bills, which have given them such nicknames as satchelhead, shovelnose, and so on. They are widely distributed ducks, and are known over most of the world; stout travelers, they are one of the few ducks that fly from Alaska to Hawaii.

By the middle of October, there are concentrations of around a quarter of a million ducks and thousands of geese at Agassiz. Besides the waterfowl that breed in northern American and Canadian prairies—half or more of the birds produced on the continent—many more come from the shores of the Arctic Ocean or Alaska, and there are whistling swans, snow and blue geese, pintails, green-winged teal, canvasbacks and scaup and many species of shorebirds. Sometimes several golden eagles come through with the geese. Bald eagles nest at Agassiz; there are also hawk owls, a rare great gray owl, and the giant Canada goose, which has been restored as a nester on the refuge.

This is northern country, with low humidity; in winter the temperature can get down to 38 or 40 degrees below zero; sometimes there are thirty inches of snow, and usually a fine show of Northern Lights. The winter birds are those hardy ones which had dropped down a little in latitude; and yellow-eyed snowy owls, those big pale daytime hunters of the tundra, are common in January and February.

*The redheaded drake has a rusty-colored head and a black breast. The female of the species often lays her eggs in another duck's nest.*

*Blue-winged teals breed only in the Temperate Zone. Because they come north quite late, they have been given the name "summer duck."*

This was good country for moose once, but by 1937 there were only three of them to be found in the vicinity. They, too, have come back; a count from the air in 1966 turned up 150 of them, and they are seen in the marshes in summer, for they are semiaquatic then, and spend most of their time in the water to get away from the heat and the flies. When they get off the refuge and onto a neighboring farm, they are a problem, for no one seems to have learned how to drive away such a powerful, unpredictable beast.

In many northern localities moose were the Indians' staff of life. Their meat was good; their hides made tough and superior leather; their horns and bones made tools; and their manes of coarse bristly hair, dyed with native dyes, were fine for embroidery. They "yard up" in the winter, sheltering in thick wooded cover, and many were killed in these yards by Indians on snowshoes strung with moose leather. Many were, and still are, killed in the mating season in the fall, when the belligerent bulls are decoyed within range by hunters using trumpets of rolled-up birchbark to imitate the squeals and grunts of amorous cows.

Deer have come back, and there are over five hundred of them now; they are held at that number by controlled hunting. Timber wolves, one of the rarest predators in the nation, appear occasionally at Agassiz. There are many muskrats; mink are common; there are a good number of beaver, and otters are present in limited numbers. The fishing isn't very good, for the pools are held to a depth of four feet, and freeze solid in the boreal winters.

*The timber wolf is rare today, although it is occasionally seen at Agassiz and the Superior National Forest in Minnesota.*

# J. Clark Salyer

The Souris, or Mouse, River, which got its name when the early French trappers in the upper North Dakota country found so many mice along its banks, makes a loop down into this country from Canada and returns to Canada again, and the J. Clark Salyer National Wildlife Refuge is on it. The refuge runs for about fifty-five miles along the river and contains about 59,000 acres, a good deal of it in marshes which were once one of the greatest areas in the nation for the slaughter of ducks for the market; ammunition was sent into it by the carload. The marshes were drained early in the century for farming, but produced so little in the way of crops that the enterprise was finally abandoned and what had once been prime wildlife habitat was left ruined and useless. The Biological Survey (now the Bureau of Sport Fisheries and Wildlife) took over the area in 1935 and built a series of dams and planted tons of seeds and tubers of aquatic plants, and the area began to recover. Salyer is now one of the best duck-production areas we have, and sometimes during migration a quarter of a million ducks are on the refuge; over 250 species of other birds have been identified there.

Much of the refuge is flat, in pools and marsh and land running off into the great grain farms that stretch to the horizon, but along the river the land rolls pleasantly. The northern portion, a good deal of which is back in native short prairie grasses again, gives lovely long views of the river and marshes, a feeling of vastness, undisturbed and beautiful. Cattle bunched on the hills in the distance

appear much like the buffalo that once existed in immense herds here and were hunted by the Indians.

Prehistoric Mound Builders once lived here; many of the French names of towns and creeks were given by the Hudson's Bay Company trappers. La Vérendrye saw it, and Alexander Henry crossed it on his way to the Missouri; Charles Cavelier camped on the river and killed four hundred buffalo out of a herd that moved past for twenty-one days. It seems to have been on the route taken by the Assiniboines and Mandans on their way to the Hudson's Bay fur posts in the eighteenth century.

Canada geese (including the giant Canada, which weighs eighteen or twenty pounds and was thought for a time to be extinct) nest here, and at migration time so many ducks come through that they spread out all over the country, and if the grain harvest is late the grain is still in farmers' fields when a hundred thousand or more ducks appear. When this happens, the refuge staff works until everybody is ready to drop — driving the birds back onto the refuge again, where much grain is grown for them.

Five species of grebes—Holboell's, horned, eared, western, and pied-billed—nest on the refuge, as well as pelicans, double-crested cormorants, black-crowned and blue herons, Franklin's gulls, and thirty-four species of shore or marsh birds. Sandhill cranes are abundant during migration, as are a great variety of perching birds, for the refuge is on the geographical line that divides eastern and western birds, and gets them from both places.

94

Salyer is one of the best places to find the rare LeConte's sparrow, and a fine nesting area for Wilson's phalaropes. These dainty little shorebirds, unlike their cousins the red and northern phalaropes, which spend most of their time at sea, like to nest in marshy spots on the prairies. They are unusual in that the females wear the bright plumage and let their husbands incubate the eggs and care for the young. As soon as the young birds are on the wing, they and their fathers join the females, which have gathered in flocks, and in August they all take their way to Argentina, Chile, or Patagonia.

A great number and variety of ducks nest on the refuge, and more of them have come in since a program of making additional potholes with explosives or bulldozers has been under way. It is hoped they will be of value in the rehabilitation of the canvasback, which was brought so low by market hunting and drainage of prairie sloughs and potholes that shooting of them wasn't allowed for a number of years. Unlike many ducks, they can't accommodate to changed conditions.

Canvasbacks have always held a special place in the affections of everyone who loves waterfowl. They are probably our fastest ducks, are powerful and direct in flight, and like to take long, high exercise flights in the mornings and evenings. They are wary but curious, and used to be "tolled" into range by small dogs trained to run back and forth between two clumps of brush to arouse their curiosity. They are divers, sometimes going down twenty to thirty feet for the wild celery bulbs and the roots of foxtail grass that make them prized beyond all ducks for the table. For this reason, they were in great demand. They sleep in rafts on open water, and market hunters shot great numbers of them at night with large guns mounted on the bows of boats. Some of them winter in Texas or Mexico, but their highest winter concentration is

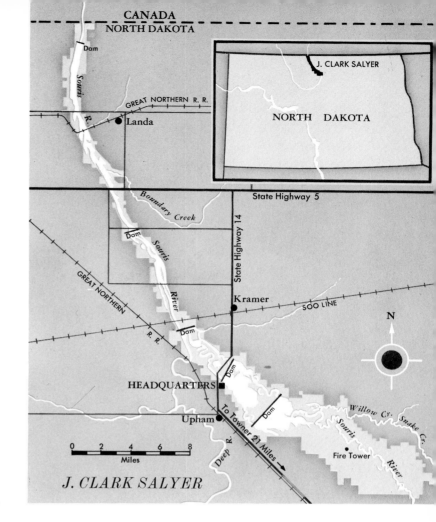

*Some of the most spectacular duck concentrations in the world are found in the vicinity of the bending, looping Souris River.*

*Like other grebes, Holboell's grebe is swift and expert in underwater maneuverings.*

*Shown here with her chicks, the eared grebe is one of five species at Salyer Refuge.*

along the Atlantic Coast, in Maryland, Virginia, and North Carolina. They don't mind rough weather, and start back north in late February or March.

Many of them, along with other ducks, nest on ponds in the Turtle Mountains, which are off the refuge but administered from it under the Wetlands Program. They wouldn't be called mountains anywhere else, being only 550 feet above the prairie, but in this flat country they are visible for a great distance. Despite their low elevation, they are really mountains in their ecology, wooded with oak, aspen, and hemlock, full of lakes, and in them the ruffed grouse—a mountain woodland bird —takes the place of the sharp-tailed grouse

not far below. Once the wintering grounds of Indians and trappers who wanted to get out of the sweep of bitter winter winds, they are full of legends; now they are the place where many prairie people go in summer for vacations, to swim and fish. Oddly enough, they give the feeling of being much higher than they are.

As on other northern refuges, the winters are cold and the night sky is often aglow with the Northern Lights. Children of the refuge personnel, shouting at their evening play, are often answered by the coyotes. Hardy visitors from farther north—snow buntings, common redpolls, northern shrikes, Bohemian wax-

LEFT ABOVE: *The ring-necked duck, so called because of a dull-colored ring at the base of its neck, is easily identified by the two white rings around its bill.*
LEFT: *The fronds of palmetto arch over an emerald-green pool on Bull's Island, part of the Cape Romain National Wildlife Refuge.*

97

wings, and snowy owls—are common, and there is an occasional golden eagle. The marshes, so lively with water birds in summer, are given over to the muskrats and their ancient enemies the minks, and raccoons, weasels, and skunks. Deer are plentiful, and there is a controlled hunting season to keep their numbers in balance; red foxes, badgers, porcupines, and rabbits hold to higher ground. Sharp-tailed grouse, diminishing in numbers over most of the country, have done well, and the introduced European gray partridge seems to find the vicinity to its liking. Both these birds stand the winters better than the ring-necked pheasant, which has also been introduced. Beaver, once trapped out, can now be found in fair numbers on many parts of the river. Within the refuge, where the number of cattle is carefully controlled, the grass flourishes, and the cattle which feed upon it bring higher prices than their neighbors' which overgraze the adjacent fields.

*A colony of double-crested cormorants, so called because of the tufts of feathers above and behind each eye, fill all but one nest in a Salyer tree. The intruder is a heron.*

# Lostwood

The Lostwood National Wildlife Refuge seems to be the loneliest and most remote place in a wide and thinly populated country. There is a wonderful air of untouched wildness about it. It is midgrass prairie, largely open to the sky, all in low, rolling hills; amid these hills are seven lakes and a great number of potholes, making it one of the best duck-breeding areas left in the nation. It is important for ducks migrating through the Central Flyway as well, has a great variety of shorebirds, and is a splendid place to find such comparatively rare species as piping plovers, Sprague's pipits, lark buntings, and Baird's sparrows; its populations of gray partridges and sharp-tailed grouse are probably the highest of any area on the Great Plains.

The pipits, at the southern end of their range, nest in the grass and sing their thin, sweet series of notes from high in the air; to hear them is one of the delights of Lostwood. The sharp-tailed grouse, unlike their cousins the vanishing prairie chickens, which liked to nest near farms, prefer to be remote from man, and can be on the refuge. They are famous for their mating dances, which take place in April. They dance on the tops of hills, and return to the same places every year. They gather at daybreak; the males spread their tails, puff out their feathers, and inflate the air sacs on their necks. They strut about, make sudden rushes, stamp their feet and leap over each other, then lower their heads and release the air in their neck sacs with a hollow booming sound. When the sun is fully up, the dancing stops and the birds disperse for the day. It has been suggested that some

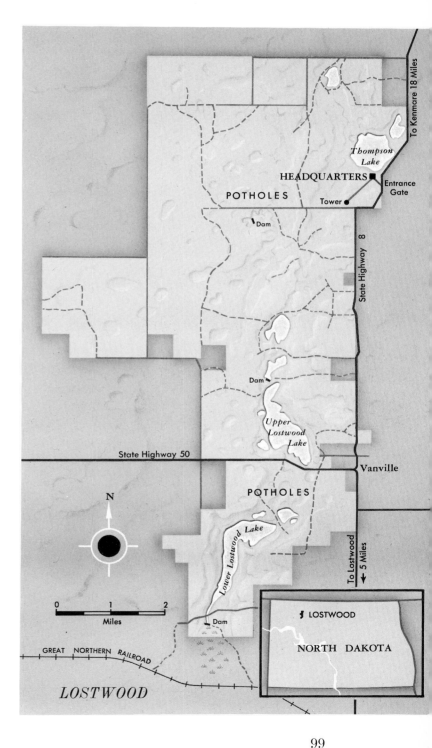

bers. Pronghorns were introduced a few years ago and have done well, and white-tailed deer are numerous.

The refuge has no recreational facilities aside from bird and animal watching; its appeal is to people who are interested in wildlife. It fulfills this desire admirably with its great variety of waterfowl, marsh birds and shorebirds, its animals, and its feeling of a

*Found on Salyer Refuge, the long-tailed weasel is able to chase a chipmunk over the branches to their outer tips.*

*This pothole, rimmed with aspen and willow, is typical of the landscape of Lostwood.*

of the Indian dances were based on these performances.

Canvasbacks and redheads, which cling tenaciously to the favorite nesting potholes of their ancestors, still find what they like at Lostwood and are there in encouraging num-

place relatively untouched and unchanged, pretty much as it was when keelboats, mackinaw boats, and, later, steamboats plied the Missouri River forty miles or so to the south to supply the fur trade and the army posts of the frontier.

# The Southeast

Region Four contains Alabama, Arkansas, Florida, Georgia, Kentucky, Louisiana, Maryland, Mississippi, North and South Carolina, Tennessee, and Virginia. It is administered from Atlanta. Most of the waterfowl that nest in the north-central states, as well as great numbers of them from the Canadian prairies and Hudson Bay, funnel into the Mississippi drainage and continue along the Mississippi Flyway through the southeast to the Gulf Coast and beyond. The region also takes in the southern portion of the Atlantic Flyway, and consequently winters a vast number of waterfowl.

There are more than fifty refuges in this region; and, except for the National Key Deer Refuge in the Florida Keys and several refuges for colony-nesting birds in Florida and Louisiana, most of them are for waterfowl. Those in Maryland, Virginia, and the Carolinas are in country that has been famous among duck and goose hunters since the settlement of the eastern seaboard. The Wheeler Refuge in Alabama is located on a Tennessee Valley Authority reservoir, and attracts thousands of waterfowl; White River Refuge in Arkansas, holding over 112,500 acres, is predominantly in timber, is flooded during late winter and spring, and holds around 250,000 waterfowl. Loxahatchee, in Florida, includes about 145,500 acres of the Everglades and holds legions of colony-nesting and other water birds, and the Sanibel Refuge on the Gulf Coast of Florida is a Mecca for shell collectors. Mattamuskeet in North Carolina holds thousands of geese, whistling swans, and ducks in winter, and Pea Island on the Outer Banks winters greater snow geese and many other creatures.

Cape Romain and Okefenokee are described in this section. They are very different from each other, and each in its way is unique and beautiful.

The Cape Romain National Wildlife Refuge, which covers about 35,000 acres and runs for fifteen miles along the South Carolina coast about fifteen miles north of Charleston, is one of the most interesting of the Atlantic Coast refuges to visit. Much of it is tidal marsh, laced with waterways, that is submerged at high tide, but Bull's Island is not.

Bull's Island is a quiet little world, easily accessible yet with a wonderful feeling of remoteness, holding within its rather small compass a surprising richness of habitat, wildlife, and flora, all largely undisturbed. It is an old barrier reef which was exposed when the land rose from the sea long ago, about six miles long and two miles wide, low and rolling, with a beautiful virgin forest of live oaks, magnolias, loblolly pines, palmettos, and other trees of the Carolina low country.

The forest, covering about a third of the island, is fascinating; almost tropical in its exuberance, it towers above you. It is draped with Spanish moss and has a thick undercover of cabbage palmetto, wax myrtle, and yaupon and American holly; in damp hollows the high old trees are looped together with climbing vines. Narrow sandy roads run through the forest; you cannot see very far into it because of the Spanish moss, cabbage palmetto, and other plants, and it is shadowy and mysterious.

You can walk for miles along the roads, always with the expectation of surprising a deer or wild turkey at any turn, and usually see some of the big black fox squirrels, and the forest echoes with the songs and flutterings of a variety of wintering songbirds which have become secretive in the thick cover. The forest is full of secret life, and has a wonderful brooding stillness until the ringing call of a big pileated woodpecker breaks it before disappearing in a flash of vivid color.

The forest isn't the only interesting thing on the island. There are hidden little ponds, green with algae, in the forest, and six larger fresh-water impoundments where the water levels are controlled by dikes and dams to provide the best conditions for wintering waterfowl. Big Jack's Creek Pond and Moccasin Pond take up most of the northern third of the island; Upper and Lower Summerhouse, House and Big Ponds are scattered through the center, and all of them are lively with egrets, herons, and thousands of ducks, of which eighteen or twenty species winter on the refuge. Alligators can usually be seen somewhere or other, or an occasional flock of Canada geese, an anhinga, or water turkey, or a glossy ibis or two. Upper Summerhouse Pond, particularly, holds a great variety of birds which can be closely approached from the cover of a wooded road. If they flush too soon, you can always sit down in cover and wait for them to return; if you find pleasure in watching this play of life before you, you will have a happy time.

The southern end of the island is difficult to get about on, being mostly in marsh cut up by tidal creeks, but the rest of it can be reached from the roads. There is one central road (running across the island from Dominick House, where the visitor brought over from the mainland in the refuge launch may stay) to the beach; the other roads cross or take off from it. Old Fort Road is on the bay side, running through the moss-draped forest, the northern marsh, and around Jack's Creek

Pond. Lighthouse Road runs through the forest on the ocean side and connects with Old Fort Road where there is the ruin of a tabby fort built long ago to keep an eye on the pirates and smugglers who liked the bay and the many escape routes from it. Sheepshead Ridge Road runs through the middle of the island and comes close to Jack's Creek and Upper Summerhouse ponds. Either Old Fort or Lighthouse Road will take you to the northern beach, which is called The Boneyard because the sea has come in and undercut the forest, and a great tangle of fallen, bleached trees lies scattered about. Multitudes of shorebirds—turnstones, knots, sanderlings, dowitchers, yellowlegs, and plovers—like this place in winter, as well as most of the Atlantic Coast's oyster catchers and long-billed curlews and marbled godwits. There are willets and dunlins on the mud flats, clapper rails in the marshes, and gulls, cormorants, and horned grebes on the beaches, and occasionally solemn brown pelicans and black skimmers—those engaging birds that fly in formation and scoop up their food with their undershot bills. The peregrine falcon, that swift hunter that has been the favorite of falconers for a thousand years or more, is sometimes a visitor.

The handsome ocean beach, wide and spacious and running uncluttered for six miles, is fine for swimming, fishing, and shell collecting; and more great loggerhead turtles come ashore here in summer to lay their eggs than anywhere else along the coast.

The wintering birds have gone north before the turtles come and summer residents have appeared. Wood ducks (probably the most handsome ducks in the world) nest secretly in hollow trees, and wood ibises, egrets, and several species of herons nest in the marshes. Many species of birds nest in the forest, and sometimes wild turkeys and deer feed on the lawn under the magnificent moss-hung live oaks in front of Dominick House.

*Among the most numerous of Cape Romain's winter shorebirds are the sanderlings, which dart back and forth with the waves, snapping up minute sea animals.*

*A female loggerhead sea turtle lumbers back to the ocean after having laid some 125 eggs in a nest upbeach. More than 600 such nests have been recorded at Cape Romain.*

Bull's Island has been known from 1670 or thereabouts, when the English landed near where Charleston is now, traded with the Indians, and established a town. Ten years later they moved it to Charleston's present location. After being owned by a number of people, it was bought by Gayer G. Dominick of New York, who later sold it to the government, for a nominal sum, to be incorporated into the refuge. Dominick House still bears his name, and the house, adjacent fire tower, and several Bureau of Sport Fisheries and Wildlife outbuildings are the only structures on the island.

A number of our refuges are large, and often many parts of them cannot be reached by the visitor. Bull's Island, however, is practically all open and within walking distance. It is an undisturbed little semitropical wilderness just outside the door, a true jewel among the Sea Islands.

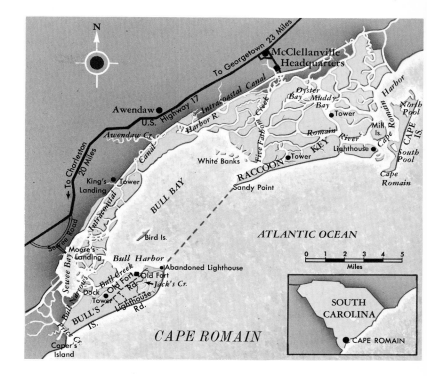

*The royal tern nests abundantly at Cape Romain
and can be found along
both the Atlantic and the Pacific coasts.
They deposit their eggs
in shallow depressions in the sand.*

The Okefenokee Swamp, which starts near Waycross, Georgia, and runs southward for thirty-eight miles to the Florida line, is a mysterious and fascinating place. Largely trackless, teeming with innumerable wild creatures, including big alligators, it is one of the most primitive swamps in the nation; there are about 331,000 acres of it in the refuge, along with 10,000 acres of adjacent upland. Unlike most swamps, it is higher than the country that surrounds it, and the Suwanee and St. Mary's rivers flow out of it; at the eastern entrance it is 120 feet above sea level, and at the western entrance 114 feet. Within its 700-odd square miles, there are great forests hung with ghostly Spanish moss, 60 lakes, 25,000 acres of islands, and 60,000 acres of "prairies"—shallow expanses of water in which a great variety of aquatic plants grow and make a flowery carpet in spring and summer.

Okefenokee is really a bog rather than a swamp, for its floor is sand, being an old sea bed, which has been covered through the centuries with peat—decomposed, waterlogged vegetation. Occasionally pieces of peat will break away from the bottom and float, and vegetation and trees take root in them. After they are grown with brush and trees, the natives call them "houses" because animals find homes on them. It was these "houses," or floating islands, finally anchored in place by roots growing down through them to the bottom, that gave the swamp its Indian name of *Owaquaphenoga,* or Trembling Earth, for they will tremble or quake when walked upon. It gives the visitor an eerie feeling to walk around on one of these "houses" with the trees trembling all around him.

Miles of boat trails, not much wider than a rowboat, wind about through the prairies, and must be mowed occasionally with a sort of underwater lawnmower. It is not at all difficult for people not familiar with the swamp to get lost in the great reaches of the prairies, for most of the "houses" look alike, and extended trips through them must be made with guides. Sometimes the boat trails open into pretty lakes, which are formed during drought years when the water gets low and the peat dries out and catches fire. The fires burn for months beneath the surface of the peat, and there is no way to put it out; these areas become lakes, or prairies, when the water rises again. A fire-control road around the swamp's perimeter, and a dike, or sill, to maintain the water level in times of drought have been built where the Suwanee River leaves the swamp. The Bureau contemplates no other changes; the swamp is to be left as it is as far as possible.

The prairies, covered by six inches to eighteen inches of water, surround the boat trails and "houses" with close-growing lily leaves, and flowers in their season. Practically all the Atlantic Flyway's species of ducks, herons, and shorebirds, as well as white and wood ibises, anhingas, kingfishers, ospreys, and red-shouldered hawks, are always to be seen in their seasons. Two hundred and one species of birds have been recorded on the refuge, and some, like the very rare ivory-billed woodpecker, formerly lived there.

An occasional otter is seen on the prairies, and deer feed on them when the water is low. They are always full of life; the fishing is good, and the views are always changing. In the middle of one of the prairies, sur-

106

*The still water of western portions of the Okefenokee Swamp
mirrors every tree and shrub.*

rounded by lilies and "houses," the visitor
feels the wildness of the place, and knows that
without a guide he would wander for days
trying to find his way out. He would have
plenty of invertebrate company, for the prairies have their share of the fifty-four species
of reptiles, thirty-two species of amphibians,
and thirty-seven species of fish that inhabit
the swamp.

The western side of Okefenokee is a different world from the eastern side. Almost
immediately after leaving the landing at
Stephen Foster State Park (reached by a
road running off U.S. Highway 44, not far
from Fargo), one is on Billy's Lake, which
is long and narrow, reflecting tall scattered
cypresses hung with Spanish moss, and from

here two ways are open. Westward there is
a boat trail leading to the sill, a watery thor-
oughfare that twists about like a tunnel
through the low trees and jungle growing out
of the water, sometimes opening into lakes
or little prairies, all backed by moss-hung
forest that is also growing through water.
The water is very dark, and everything is
reflected on its ebony surface with such fidel-
ity that after looking at it for a while one
seems to float bodiless and lost between the
reflected trees and sky, and is unable to tell
which is real and which is reflection.

Near the eastward end of Billy's lake the
boat turns northward into a narrow channel,
and is soon among tall cypress hung with
moss and growing close together. This is the
most dreamlike place in Okefenokee. Time

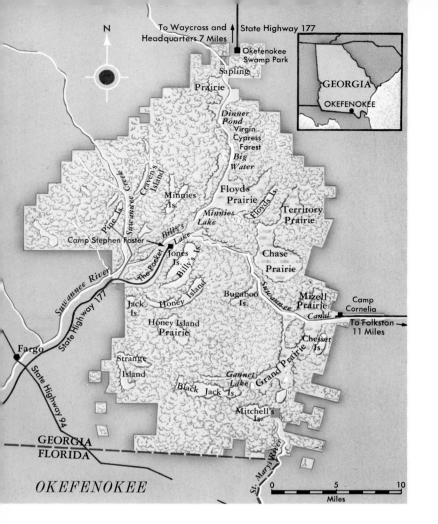

*The only way to see the more remote parts of Okefenokee is by guided boat tours.*

doesn't seem to have touched or changed it; it seems like a place for sorcerers and wizards. The alligators, some of them twelve to fourteen feet long, lie like dark logs among the lilies along the boat trail, and vanish in a flurry when the boat comes too close. Jewett Hall, the biological technician who took us about, was born in the swamp and has lived most of his life in it. He stopped the boat where an alligator had submerged, and "grunted him up" by calling in alligator language. The lily pads stirred three feet from the boat; the cold ridged eyes appeared and looked at us, and, not liking what they saw, vanished again. We didn't see that one again, but we saw many others. When they mate in the spring, they make a great bellowing, joining the chorus of the swamp's millions of frogs. Before we started again, a barred owl, hidden nearby in a moss-hung cypress, gave his eight staccato hoots in objection to our presence.

The red wolf, a small species which may still be found on several of our southern refuges, is probably extinct in Okefenokee; the Florida puma may still occur as a transient, and there are still black bears about. Most of the forty-one species of mammals are hard to find, for travel is practically all by boat along the trails, and the underbrush is thick. Aside from the birds, alligators are probably seen more often than any other creature. People are in little danger from them, but the converse isn't true; their hides are so valuable that poachers are always after them at night, and the refuge staff is kept busy protecting them. If we want to keep our alligators, we must make more stringent laws to prohibit the trade in alligator leather.

There is an enormous variety of plants in the swamp: 91 species of trees, 89 of shrubs and vines, 10 of ferns and club mosses, 51 of mosses and liverworts, 65 of sedges, and 315 of flowering shrubs. Their great richness and variety, as well as the richness of the animal life and the unspoiled beauty of the place, make Okefenokee unique. It is a wonderful place to visit in spring, autumn, and winter, and I hope that it will be left just as it is.

Okefenokee has had an interesting history. Probably the first white people to see it were three hundred men led by the Spaniard Pánfilo de Narváez in 1528, and only four men returned from this expedition. One of these was Cabeza de Vaca, who wrote of Indian attacks and the immense difficulty of getting about. In 1539 Hernando de Soto made a sortie with five hundred men into the vicinity, and may have got to Okefenokee. He found "a great morass . . . bordered by huge and lofty trees, dense underwood or thorns and brambles . . . a perfect barrier." He battled the Indians, and "fought to the waist in water, stumbling among thorns, twisted roots and sunken trunks of trees." Anyone who has seen the country will find his imagination appalled by the struggles of the Spaniards, weighed down by their armor and lost among the snakes, alligators, and the riot of vegetation.

The aboriginal Indians were an unknown tribe which left burial mounds on many of the islands. They were probably the Tomucuas, who were barbarously treated and finally exterminated by the Spaniards and early English settlers. When the Americans moved in, in the early nineteenth century, the Seminoles were there, and caused so much trouble that the army was sent in in 1838 to subdue them. After struggling about in "one of the most horrible swamps on the face of the earth," the army found and burned a village from which the Seminoles had fled, and struggled out again, "wet, hungry, and nearly dead from fatigue." The Seminoles fled to Florida, and after that there were no more Indian troubles.

The earliest white settler was a man

*The anhinga, or snakebird, rests with its wings outstretched to dry in the sun. Snakebirds are excellent underwater swimmers.*

named James Lee, who built a house on Billy's Island, near Stephen Foster State Park, in 1850. Several other families moved in later; they all lived practically cut off from the world, farming a little, trapping fur, shooting alligators, and hunting and fishing. They were apparently very healthy, for there never has been in Okefenokee the malaria and other swamp diseases that vexed the low country of the rest of Georgia and the Carolinas; they were superb trackers and woodsmen, and wonderful guides for outsiders. A number of tales of fugitives from the law and escaped Civil War prisoners hiding in the swamp are probably untrue, for life in the swamp was too difficult for strangers.

*The cottonmouth water moccasin is an adept swimmer and feeds primarily on the swamp's frogs and small mammals, birds' eggs, and birds.*

The vast amount of timber in the swamp (some of the cypresses were estimated to be from four hundred to nine hundred years old)

*One of the swamp's most amusing creatures is the eastern spadefoot toad. Unlike other toads, it has smooth instead of warty skin.*

had always interested lumbermen, and in 1891 a company was formed to drain the place and lumber it. After a million dollars was spent and a canal eleven and a half miles long was dug into the prairies on the eastern side, the project was given up; the canal is still there, and is kept open by the Bureau as a means of getting about. Later, a Philadelphia lumber company built about thirty-five miles of railroad on pilings into the swamp, and by 1927, when work was stopped, about 423,000,000 feet of timber were taken out. The scars left by this operation are now largely hidden by subsequent tree growth.

Scientists from Cornell University, who began a series of investigations in the swamp in 1909, felt that its uniqueness and beauty should be preserved; they were joined by a number of conservation organizations, and finally the Georgia legislature asked the federal government to take over the swamp. This was done in 1936, and the refuge was established in 1937.

# *The Northeast*

Region Five contains Maine, Vermont, New Hampshire, Massachusetts, Connecticut, Rhode Island, West Virginia, New York, Pennsylvania, New Jersey, and Delaware. It is administered from Boston. A great number of waterfowl on their way to their wintering grounds pass through the Atlantic Flyway in this region. They fly either along the coast, on a diagonal from James Bay, at the foot of Hudson Bay, or on another diagonal from the eastern Canadian prairies, across the Great Lakes. The northeastern refuges don't winter a great many birds, but they are important because they serve as stepping-stones to the south.

Few of these refuges are very large in area, but they are necessary in a section that was settled so early in our history and is so highly industrialized and thickly populated. Monomoy is a coastal barrier island within the boundaries of Chatham Township on Cape Cod; the island is widely known for the great number of different species of birds that migrate through it in the fall and spring, and about a million eider ducks and scoters use the surrounding waters in fall and winter. The 6,000-acre Great Swamp Refuge, with trails through its undisturbed wooded swamps and upland timber, isn't far from New York City, and is easily reached. The Iroquois Refuge in New York, 10,800 acres in extent, holds thousands of ducks and geese in the spring and fall, and a high year-round population of birds and mammals. Brigantine in New Jersey is attractive to bird watchers all year for its many species, and is also close to centers of high population. The Introduction (page 11) includes some description of Bombay Hook in Delaware and my experiences there, and Moosehorn in Maine is described in the following pages.

*Two Canada geese wing through a wooded swamp at Iroquois
National Wildlife Refuge in New York.*

The Moosehorn Refuge, divided into two units, is in the northeast corner of Maine. The larger Baring Unit is near Calais (pronounced "callous"), which is on the St. Croix River that separates New Brunswick and Maine, and the Edmunds Unit meets salt water on Cobscook Bay. Quoddy Head, the nation's easternmost point, is a few miles east of it. Tides rise and fall twenty-eight feet at Calais, the highest tides in the continental United States; winters are cold, and there is usually plenty of snow.

There are more trees than people in this country, and it has many beautiful lakes; once there was a great stand of white pines here, growing over two hundred feet high and six feet or more in diameter, but they are hard to find now because Calais became a lumbering center early in our history and most of them were cut down.

Moosehorn is different from most of the other refuges along the East Coast, which were built around waterfowl marshes. It is mostly upland covered with second-growth timber, brush, and clumps of white birch and aspen among the dark evergreens which run down to most of the lakes and the sea. The coastline is charming, wandering and indented, full of little bays, secret coves, and tiny offshore islands. There are piles of lobster pots in most of the yards in the few villages.

The land on the refuge rolls gently, and there are lakes, fresh-water marshes, streams that are called "flowages" if they have been dammed by men or beavers, and northern sphagnum bogs that are like huge cushions, soft and springy when one walks on them,

where low wild cranberry, blueberry, and black spruce trees grow. About 15,000 of the 22,565 acres are timbered, and controlled lumbering and timber-stand improvement are under way.

Deer on the refuge, once too numerous, have been brought into balance with the food supply, and are kept there by controlled hunting; there are many black bears, which are numerous in Maine because they like plenty of elbow room. The most spectacular animals are the moose; there are a few big bulls, and at rare intervals one of them will wander onto the highway and offer to take on all comers. Standing six or seven feet high, and weighing half a ton or more, with antlers sometimes spreading sixty inches, and of uncertain temper and immense strength, they find few people who try to push them around. We went looking for one with the refuge manager, searching in the marshes and crawling around the bogs, but couldn't find one. There were big footprints along the refuge roads where the moose had been strolling earlier in the morning after a rainy night, and we had to be satisfied with those.

The refuge has its share of bobcats, snowshoe hares, red foxes, otter, mink, muskrats, weasels, and porcupines; there are flying and red and gray squirrels, and harbor seals along the shore of the Edmunds Unit. Beaver have done well on the refuge, and the fisher, which has been very rare for a long time, seems to be increasing.

This creature is a large, dark weasel with a bushy tail; it is about three feet long, and weighs up to eighteen pounds. Once it was

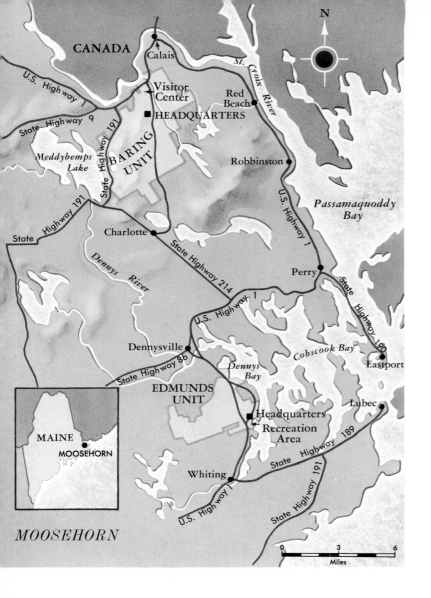

MOOSEHORN

*At the Baring Unit of Moosehorn, the land rolls gently and is dotted with natural lakes and beaver dams, like the one shown here.*

found in evergreen forests all across the northern part of the continent and down into the Alleghenies, the Rockies, and the coast ranges of the West, but it was almost trapped out for its fur. Like all weasels it is an animal of boundless energy, at home in trees or on the ground, and a fine swimmer; it has been said that a pine marten can catch a squirrel and that a fisher can catch a pine marten, which gives an idea of its agility. It is a clever trap robber, a savage fighter, and will eat anything; it has been known to kill animals as large as deer, and is one of the very few animals that makes a habit of catching porcupines. When they eat quills, the quills pass through their intestines without penetrating the mucous lining; quills in their skins work out without causing inflammation, swelling, or suppuration, as they do in other animals. George Linklater, for many years a chief trader for the Hudson's Bay Company, once said that he had never seen a fisher pelt without quills in it, and in all his experience had found only one fisher that had apparently been damaged by a porcupine. It is a most unusual creature.

Two hundred species of birds have been identified on the refuge, and many of them nest there. Several marshes have been improved for waterfowl, which has induced black ducks, wood ducks, and green-and-blue-winged teal to nest. Ring-necked ducks, which don't nest on many refuges, are abundant. They migrate in midfall; many go to Louisiana, but most of them go to the southern part of the Atlantic Flyway or to Mexico. The calling of loons, so characteristic of northern lakes, and sounding like crazy laughter, is often heard. Bald eagles are seen at Moosehorn all year round, and the refuge has eight

*With velvet hanging from his antlers,*
*a male moose feeds*
*in a marshy pool. The antlers may grow*
*to widths of six feet across.*
*In late summer,*
*the velvet, or soft fur covering,*
*begins to peel, exposing the bone beneath.*

The adaptable black bears have done well at Moosehorn, as in all wooded country. The young, born every other year, number one to four.

Ready to leap, RIGHT, a flying squirrel selects a landing site which may be as much as 125 feet away. In midflight, CENTER, the squirrel uses its tail as a guiding rudder and, FAR RIGHT, makes a four-point landing at its destination.

116

nesting species of hawks, as well as eight species of owls; the big snowy owl and the boreal owl, both rare in the East, are seen in winter. Ravens are more common than crows, and there is a great variety of warblers and vireos, as well as twelve species of sparrows. There are ruffed grouse and occasionally spruce grouse, evening and pine grosbeaks, and tree sparrows; Lapland longspurs from the northern tundra appear in winter. The Canada jay, often called "whisky-jack," the camp robber, a character full of amusing antics, is often seen.

Although the refuge is important to ducks, one of the main reasons for it is the woodcock, that rather mysterious creature which hunters of our native birds love so well. Moosehorn is in the center of its northeastern nesting grounds. It is a chunky bird about the size of a quail, so well camouflaged that it is very difficult to see among fallen leaves and ground litter. It has a long bill with a flexible tip with which it probes in soft ground for worms; its big dark eyes are set high in its head, and it has a short tail and rounded wings. Because it won't fly until nearly stepped upon, it is a good bird for training pointing dogs; its flight is swift and erratic.

The woodcock feeds along spring runs and in damp places at night or in half-light, spends the days in higher cover, and migrates at night, returning to the same covers year after year. It is even crepuscular in its mating, which occurs in late April or early May. A male will pick out a fairly open spot that he likes, and when the intensity of light is just right will begin to strut and utter a metallic, nasal "peentl," which carries a long way, and occasionally chuckle to himself. Every five minutes or so he jumps into the air, climbs in a batlike spiral from one hundred to three hundred feet, and at the top of his pitch sings a beautiful sweet, warbling song. At the short song's end, he dives recklessly down to within twenty feet or so of the ground, flutters softly to a landing, and begins to strut again. The females come to him.

Woodcock are trapped for banding in various ways at Moosehorn, for a project

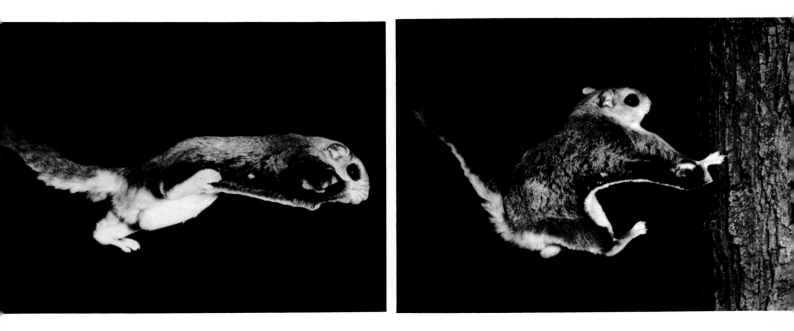

*The male fisher, shown here looking out of a hollow tree, has conspicuous whitish hairs on its head and shoulders. The fisher is easily distinguished from a fox, which it resembles, by its rounded ears.*

*The fisher's favorite food is the porcupine, a large rodent which sometimes reaches a length of three feet. Except for underparts and portions of the face, the porcupine's body is covered with some 30,000 quills.*

covering several years is under way to study the bird and find out more about him. Envelopes are also sent out from Patuxent every year to known woodcock hunters, who are asked to send in a wing from every bird they shoot. Biologists who examine these wings can tell whether the bird it came from was an old or young one, whether the population is holding up, and what the proportion of young to old birds is. For a while it was feared that pesticides from the worms woodcock eat was thinning their numbers, but this doesn't seem to be so.

In the Moosehorn country the scars of clean lumbering and the fires that followed it around the turn of the century have in a measure healed; it is wonderfully wild and uncluttered, and there is enough wilderness and clean air for anybody. This is surprising, for the vicinity has been known for a long time. The Norsemen probably saw it in the year 1000; the Cabots mapped the coast around 1498; Captain John Smith mapped it again in 1614; and the Pilgrims established a trading post at nearby Machias in 1629; most of the expense of the Mayflower Expedition was paid for with furs from this post. A great deal of smuggling went on across the Maine border in the War of 1812, and there were pirates off the coast. An interesting thing is that the local Indians, Penobscots and Passamaquoddies, in the days when they and the settlers were murdering one another, never scalped their victims until English officers did it first and showed them how.

I feel that a book like this is impossible to finish, for more refuges are being opened as time goes on, and people who take pleasure in seeing them and the birds and animals they contain would like to hear about them. There are many more places one would like to go and many more creatures one would like to see. America is a many-splendored place; who but the most fortunate can explore it as fully as he wishes?

Many people are content to spend their lives in cities; the rest of us are moved by natural beauty and need it. We are very fortunate that there were a few men years ago who foresaw that steps would have to be taken to preserve as much of it as they could, and set about to do this. What our heritage of wildlife and unique places would be now if it hadn't been for them isn't pleasant to imagine.

Unlike the majority of national parks, forests, monuments and wilderness areas that we have managed to set aside before they were gone, the refuges are in many cases almost re-creations. Places that were despoiled and creatures that were hovering on the edge of extinction have been brought back in some degree, and the work is still going on. There is plenty yet to do. In 1966 the Bureau of Sport Fisheries and Wildlife published a list (Resource Publication 34, Government Printing Office) of rare and endangered mammals, birds, reptiles, amphibians, and fish, and the list is a long one. It opens with an enumeration of creatures that have become extinct since 1768 and includes such species as the Plains wolf, the eastern elk, the passenger pigeon, the Badlands bighorn, the Carolina parakeet, the heath hen, and many of the unique birds of Hawaii.

This list will grow longer and could reach out to include the large whales, the timber wolf and grizzly bear in the conterminous United States, the California condor, the Everglades kite, the whooping crane and many others unless the work that has been done continues and has wide support. We will leave our world a poorer place for our children and the other people who will come after us if we fail to make the effort to conserve these creatures.

The Bureau of Sport Fisheries and Wildlife is the agency charged with the preservation of our wildlife and many unique places on a national scale, but the Bureau can't do this alone. The job is too big in a civilization as complicated as ours has become. The success of the enterprise depends upon help from other government, state and local agencies, private organizations, and, ultimately, individuals. To succeed it must have the co-operation of you and me, of all of us.

*The everglade kite subsists entirely on one species of snail, which feeds on the marshy vegetation of the Florida Everglades. Drainage of the Florida swamplands for development has caused a decrease in the snails' habitat, and thus threatens to destroy the kite.*

# Appendix: The National Wildlife Refuges in Brief

The National Wildlife Refuge System contains over 300 areas, but only about 170 have personnel resident on or near the project. These are the refuges most persons visit.

The refuges listed here give a sampling of the wildlife to be seen. Bird and mammal checklists, containing more detailed accounts of wildlife, have been prepared for nearly all these refuges, and may be obtained by writing to the refuge manager. The general location of a refuge may be found on the map on pages 12–13. Detailed information about the best way to reach the area is available from the refuge.

Information concerning camping facilities is also available for most refuges. In this guide one asterisk (*) following the name of a refuge denotes camping facilities on the refuge. Two asterisks (**) indicate that by writing to the refuge, information may be obtained about camping facilities nearest the refuge.

Some refuge managers have responsibilities for managing other nearby refuges. These are listed here at the end of an account. Permission should be secured from the manager before entering these refuges. Bird and mammal checklists and information on camping are available from the administering refuge.

Many refuges have been excluded from this guide because of their small size, their relative inaccessibility, or lack of personnel and visitor facilities.

## ALABAMA
CHOCTAW NATIONAL WILDLIFE REFUGE** • 4,200 acres attractive to Canada geese, ducks, mourning doves. Box 325, Jackson, Ala. 36545.

EUFAULA NATIONAL WILDLIFE REFUGE** • 7,900 acres in Alabama and 3,200 acres in Georgia supporting ducks, Canada geese, wading and marsh birds, bobwhites. Box 258, Eufaula, Ala. 36027.

WHEELER NATIONAL WILDLIFE REFUGE** • 35,000 acres for bobwhites, mourning doves, opossums, ducks, geese. Box 1643, Decatur, Ala. 35601.

## ARIZONA
HAVASU LAKE NATIONAL WILDLIFE REFUGE** • 22,000 acres supporting Canada geese, ducks, herons, egrets, Yuma clapper rails, white-winged doves, desert bighorn. Box A, Needles, Calif. 92363.

IMPERIAL NATIONAL WILDLIFE REFUGE* • 43,000 acres for Canada geese, ducks, herons, egrets, Yuma clapper rails, white-winged doves, desert bighorn. Box 1032, Yuma, Ariz. 85364. Administered from Imperial: Kofa Game Range, 660,000 acres.

## ARKANSAS
BIG LAKE NATIONAL WILDLIFE REFUGE** • 9,900 acres attracting ducks, geese, quail, muskrat, white-tailed deer. Box 65, Manila, Ark. 72442.

HOLLA BEND NATIONAL WILDLIFE REFUGE** • 4,000 acres supporting ducks, geese, herons, bobwhites. Box 746, Russellville, Ark. 72801.

WAPANOCCA NATIONAL WILDLIFE REFUGE** • 5,500 acres for woodcock, herons, wild turkeys, white-tailed deer, black bears, ducks, geese. Box 308, 704 South Jefferson St., De Witt, Ark. 72042.

## CALIFORNIA
KERN NATIONAL WILDLIFE REFUGE** • 10,600 acres for Canada geese and ducks. Box 219, Delano, Calif. 93215. Administered from Kern: Pixley National Wildlife Refuge, 4,300 acres.

MERCED NATIONAL WILDLIFE REFUGE* • 2,500 acres accommodating ducks, sandhill cranes, and snow, white-fronted, "cackling" Canada, and Ross' geese. Box 854, Merced, Calif. 95341.

MODOC NATIONAL WILDLIFE REFUGE* • 6,000 acres supporting "western" Canada geese and ducks. Box 1439, Alturas, Calif. 96101.

SACRAMENTO NATIONAL WILDLIFE REFUGE** • 10,775 acres attracting pheasants, white-tailed kites, ducks, and snow, "cackling" Canada, and Ross' geese. Box 311, Route 1, Willows, Calif. 95988. Administered from Sacramento: Colusa National Wildlife Refuge, 4,040 acres; Delevan National Wildlife Refuge, 5,600 acres; Farallon National Wildlife Refuge, 91 acres; Sutter National Wildlife Refuge, 2,600 acres.

SALTON SEA NATIONAL WILDLIFE REFUGE** • 36,400 acres attracting geese, ducks, including the fulvous tree duck, and shorebirds. Box 247, Calipatria, Calif. 92233.

TULE LAKE NATIONAL WILDLIFE REFUGE** • 37,000 acres supporting white-fronted, "cackling" Canada, snow, and Ross' geese, pheasants, muskrat.

Box 74, Route 1, Tulelake, Calif. 96134. Administered from Tule Lake: Clear Lake National Wildlife Refuge, 33,500 acres; Klamath Forest National Wildlife Refuge, 15,000 acres; Lower Klamath National Wildlife Refuge, 22,800 acres; Upper Klamath National Wildlife Refuge, 12,500 acres.

## COLORADO
MONTE VISTA NATIONAL WILDLIFE REFUGE* • 13,900 acres for geese, ducks, sandhill cranes. Administered from Monte Vista: Alamosa National Wildlife Refuge, 5,300 acres.

## DELAWARE
BOMBAY HOOK NATIONAL WILDLIFE REFUGE** • 16,-300 acres attracting black ducks, blue-winged teal, gadwalls, greater snow geese, white-tailed deer. Route 1, Box 147, Smyrna, Del. 19977. Administered from Bombay Hook: Prime Hook National Wildlife Refuge, 4,100 acres.

## FLORIDA
CHASSAHOWITZKA NATIONAL WILDLIFE REFUGE** • 30,700 acres for waterfowl, Florida sandhill cranes, limpkins, white ibises. Route 1, Box 153, Homosassa, Fla. 32646. Administered from Chassahowitzka: Cedar Keys National Wildlife Refuge, 375 acres.

J. N. "DING" DARLING NATIONAL WILDLIFE REFUGE* • 3,000 acres accommodating waterfowl, herons, roseate spoonbills, alligators. Lighthouse Quarters 1, Sanibel, Fla. 33957.

LAKE WOODRUFF NATIONAL WILDLIFE REFUGE** • 16,450 acres for ducks, white-tailed deer, wild turkeys. Box 488, De Leon Springs, Fla. 32028.

LOXAHATCHEE NATIONAL WILDLIFE REFUGE** • 145,525 acres attracting waterfowl, herons, egrets, everglade kites, Florida sandhill cranes, limpkins. Box 278, Route 1, Delray Beach, Fla. 33444.

MERRITT ISLAND NATIONAL WILDLIFE REFUGE* • 46,500 acres for waterfowl, herons, egrets, dusky seaside sparrows. Box 956, Titusville, Fla. 32780. Administered from Merritt Island: Pelican Island National Wildlife Refuge, 616 acres.

NATIONAL KEY DEER REFUGE* • 6,745 acres supporting key white-tailed deer, roseate spoonbills, great white herons, white-crowned pigeons. Big Pine, Fla. 33040. Administered from Key Deer: Great White Heron National Wildlife Refuge and Key West National Wildlife Refuge, both about 2,000 acres.

ST. MARKS NATIONAL WILDLIFE REFUGE** • 65,100 acres attracting Canada geese, ducks, herons, limpkins, wild turkeys, white-tailed deer. Box 68, St. Marks, Fla. 32355.

## GEORGIA
OKEFENOKEE NATIONAL WILDLIFE REFUGE* • 341,-000 acres supporting sandhill cranes, white ibises, swallow-tailed kites, white-tailed deer, river otters, alligators. Box 117, Waycross, Ga. 31501.

PIEDMONT NATIONAL WILDLIFE REFUGE* • 33,300 acres for waterfowl, bobwhites, mourning doves, wild turkeys; beaver. Round Oak, Ga. 31080.

SAVANNAH NATIONAL WILDLIFE REFUGE • 5,555 acres in Georgia and 7,600 acres in South Carolina for ducks. Route 1, Hardeeville, S.C. 29927.

## IDAHO
CAMAS NATIONAL WILDLIFE REFUGE** • 10,656 acres attracting Canada geese, whistling swans, long-billed curlews, pronghorn. Hamer, Idaho 83425.

DEER FLAT NATIONAL WILDLIFE REFUGE** • 11,400 acres supporting Canada geese, ducks, white pelicans, pheasants, gulls. Box 355, Route 1, Nampa, Idaho 83651.

GRAYS LAKE NATIONAL WILDLIFE REFUGE** • 13,000 acres attracting Canada geese, redheads, canvasbacks, ruddy ducks, greater sandhill cranes. Box 837, Soda Springs, Idaho 83276.

KOOTENAI NATIONAL WILDLIFE REFUGE** • 2,767 acres for waterfowl. Star Route 1, Bonners Ferry, Idaho 83805.

MINIDOKA NATIONAL WILDLIFE REFUGE • 25,630 acres accommodating Canada geese, ducks, whistling swans, sage grouse. Route 4, Minidoka Dam, Rupert, Idaho 83350.

## ILLINOIS
CHAUTAUQUA NATIONAL WILDLIFE REFUGE** • 4,500 acres for mallards, wood ducks, bald eagles. Rural Route 2, Havana, Ill. 62644.

CRAB ORCHARD NATIONAL WILDLIFE REFUGE* • 42,-825 acres attracting Canada, blue, and snow geese, ducks, bobwhites, white-tailed deer. Box J, Carterville, Ill. 62918.

MARK TWAIN NATIONAL WILDLIFE REFUGE** • 24,-000 acres supporting ducks, geese, herons, bald eagles, terns. Box 225, Quincy, Ill. 62302. Administered from Mark Twain: Clarence Cannon National Wildlife Refuge, 3,670 acres.

## INDIANA
MUSCATATUCK NATIONAL WILDLIFE REFUGE** • 8,000 acres for waterfowl. Box 531, Seymour, Ind. 47274.

## IOWA
DE SOTO NATIONAL WILDLIFE REFUGE** • 7,800 acres for ducks and geese. Route 1B, Missouri Valley, Iowa 51555.

UNION SLOUGH NATIONAL WILDLIFE REFUGE** •

2,077 acres for ducks, geese, game birds. Box 36, Titonka, Iowa 50480.

## KANSAS

FLINT HILLS NATIONAL WILDLIFE REFUGE** • 22,000 acres for blue and snow geese and mallards. Box 213, Burlington, Kans. 66839.

KIRWIN NATIONAL WILDLIFE REFUGE* • 10,800 acres attracting white-fronted geese, ducks, sandhill cranes, shorebirds. Box 125, Kirwin, Kans. 67644.

QUIVIRA NATIONAL WILDLIFE REFUGE* • 20,380 acres supporting waterfowl, bobwhites, bald eagles. Box G, Stafford, Kans. 67578.

## LOUISIANA

CATAHOULA NATIONAL WILDLIFE REFUGE* • 5,300 acres attracting waterfowl and white pelicans. Box 638, Jonesville, La. 71343.

DELTA NATIONAL WILDLIFE REFUGE • 48,800 acres for blue and snow geese, ducks, egrets, shorebirds, alligators. Venice, La. 70091.

SABINE NATIONAL WILDLIFE REFUGE** • 142,850 acres accommodating blue and snow geese, mottled ducks, roseate spoonbills, glossy ibises, and alligators. MRH 107, Sulphur, La. 70663.

## MAINE

MOOSEHORN NATIONAL WILDLIFE REFUGE** • The Baring Unit, 16,000 acres, and the Edmunds Unit, 6,500 acres, support woodcock, black and ring-necked ducks, snowshoe hares, white-tailed deer, and a few moose. Box 285, Calais, Maine 04619.

## MARYLAND

BLACKWATER NATIONAL WILDLIFE REFUGE** • 11,-200 acres supporting Canada geese, ducks, muskrat, bald eagles, Delmarva Peninsula fox squirrels. Route 2, Cambridge, Md. 21613.

EASTERN NECK NATIONAL WILDLIFE REFUGE** • 2,283 acres for ducks, geese, swans, white-tailed deer. Route 2, Box 193, Rock Hall, Md. 21661.

## MASSACHUSETTS

GREAT MEADOWS NATIONAL WILDLIFE REFUGE** • 3,800 acres attracting wood and black ducks, mallards, teal, songbirds. 110 Great Road, Bedford, Mass. 01730. Administered from Great Meadows: Monomoy National Wildlife Refuge, 2,700 acres.

PARKER RIVER NATIONAL WILDLIFE REFUGE** • 4,650 acres supporting greater scaup, black ducks, Canada geese, shorebirds. Northern Boulevard, Plum Island, Newburyport, Mass. 01950. Administered from Parker River: Coastal Maine National Wildlife Refuge, 6,000 acres.

## MICHIGAN

SENEY NATIONAL WILDLIFE REFUGE** • 95,500 acres attracting Canada geese, sandhill cranes, spruce and ruffed grouse, white-tailed deer, river otters. Star Route, Seney, Mich. 49883. Administered from Seney: Huron National Wildlife Refuge, five islands totaling 147 acres.

SHIAWASSEE NATIONAL WILDLIFE REFUGE** • 8,850 acres for geese, ducks, pheasants, bobwhites, white-tailed deer, whistling swans, 6975 Mower Road, Route 1, Saginaw, Mich. 48601.

## MINNESOTA

AGASSIZ NATIONAL WILDLIFE REFUGE** • 61,500 acres attracting geese, ducks, sharp-tailed grouse, a few moose and black bears. Middle River, Minn. 56737.

RICE LAKE NATIONAL WILDLIFE REFUGE** • 17,000 acres supporting great blue herons, double-crested cormorants, ring-necked ducks, beaver. Box 190, McGregor, Minn. 55760.

SHERBURNE NATIONAL WILDLIFE REFUGE** • 30,000 acres for ducks and geese. 119 Fifth Ave. S., Princeton, Minn. 55371.

TAMARAC NATIONAL WILDLIFE REFUGE* • 38,900 acres accommodating waterfowl, white-tailed deer, ruffed grouse, muskrat, beaver. Rural Route, Rochert, Minn. 56578.

UPPER MISSISSIPPI RIVER WILDLIFE AND FISH REFUGE • 195,000 acres in Wisconsin, Iowa, Minnesota, and Illinois comprising one of the most notable wildlife areas in North America. 405 Exchange Building, Box 226, Winona, Minn. 55987.

## MISSISSIPPI

GULF ISLAND NATIONAL WILDLIFE REFUGES** • Island refuges for waterfowl and sea turtles. Box 165, Biloxi, Miss. 39533.

NOXUBEE NATIONAL WILDLIFE REFUGE** • 45,850 acres attracting wild turkeys, waterfowl, white-tailed deer, bobwhites, mourning doves. Route 1, Brooksville, Miss. 39739.

YAZOO NATIONAL WILDLIFE REFUGE* • Over 9,300 acres for Canada geese, ducks, herons, mourning doves. Box 296, Route 1, Hollandale, Miss. 38748.

## MISSOURI

MINGO NATIONAL WILDLIFE REFUGE** • 21,650 acres supporting geese, ducks, herons, raccoons, bobcats, and several species of snakes. Route 1, Box 9A, Puxico, Mo. 63960.

SQUAW CREEK NATIONAL WILDLIFE REFUGE** • 6,800 acres attracting blue and snow geese, American widgeons, green-winged teal, gadwalls, white pelicans. Box 101, Mound City, Mo. 64470.

SWAN LAKE NATIONAL WILDLIFE REFUGE** • 10,700 acres supporting Canada geese, ducks, and a few prairie chickens. Box 68, Sumner, Mo. 64681.

## MONTANA

BENTON LAKE NATIONAL WILDLIFE REFUGE** • 12,-400 acres for geese, ducks, shorebirds, pheasants. Box 2624, Great Falls, Mont. 59401. Administered from Benton Lake: Pishkun National Wildlife Refuge, 8,200 acres; Willow Creek National Wildlife Refuge, 3,100 acres.

BOWDOIN NATIONAL WILDLIFE REFUGE** • 15,500 acres attracting Canada geese, ducks, white pelicans, herons, cormorants, sage grouse, pronghorn. Box J, Malta, Mont. 59538. Waterfowl refuges administered from Bowdoin: Black Coulee National Wildlife Refuge, 1,500 acres; Creedman Coulee National Wildlife Refuge, 2,700 acres; Lake Thibadeau National Wildlife Refuge, 3,500 acres; Hewitt Lake National Wildlife Refuge, 1,680 acres.

CHARLES M. RUSSELL NATIONAL WILDLIFE RANGE* • 951,000 acres supporting sharp-tailed and sage grouse, bighorn sheep, elk, mountain plover, prairie dogs. Box 110, Lewiston, Mont. 59457. Waterfowl refuges administered from Charles M. Russell: Hailstone National Wildlife Refuge, 2,240 acres; Halfbreed Lake National Wildlife Refuge, 3,100 acres; Lake Mason National Wildlife Refuge, 19,150 acres; War Horse National Wildlife Refuge, 3,200 acres.

MEDICINE LAKE NATIONAL WILDLIFE REFUGE* • 31,-450 acres attracting geese, ducks, sandhill cranes, sharp-tailed grouse, shorebirds, gulls, terns, muskrat. Medicine Lake, Mont. 59247. Administered from Medicine Lake: Lamesteer National Wildlife Refuge, 800 acres.

NATIONAL BISON RANGE** • 18,540 acres for buffalo, elk, pronghorn, deer, bighorn sheep. Moiese, Mont. 59824.

RAVALLI NATIONAL WILDLIFE REFUGE** • 2,700 acres for Canada geese and ducks. No. 5 Third St., Stevensville, Mont. 59870.

RED ROCK LAKES NATIONAL WILDLIFE REFUGE • 40,-000 acres supporting trumpeter swans, Shiras' moose, grayling, pronghorn. Monida, Mont. 59744.

## NEBRASKA

CRESCENT LAKE NATIONAL WILDLIFE REFUGE** • 46,000 acres attracting geese, ducks, sandhill cranes, long-billed curlews, prairie chickens. Star Route 30178, Ellsworth, Nebr. 69340. Administered from Crescent Lake: North Platte National Wildlife Refuge, 5,000 acres.

FORT NIOBRARA NATIONAL WILDLIFE REFUGE** • 19,100 acres accommodating buffalo, Texas longhorns, elk, sharp-tailed grouse, beaver. Hidden Timber Route, Valentine, Nebr. 69201.

VALENTINE NATIONAL WILDLIFE REFUGE** • 71,500 acres supporting ducks, geese, sharp-tailed grouse,

pheasants, shorebirds, pronghorn. Kennedy Star Route, Valentine, Nebr. 69201.

## NEVADA

DESERT NATIONAL WILDLIFE RANGE** • 1,500,000 acres supporting desert bighorn, mule deer, Gambel's quail, pronghorn. 1500 North Decatur Boulevard, Las Vegas, Nev. 89108. Administered from Desert: Pahranagat National Wildlife Refuge, 5,400 acres.

RUBY LAKE NATIONAL WILDLIFE REFUGE** • 37,200 acres for Canada geese, ducks, sage grouse, sandhill cranes, shorebirds, trumpeter swans. Ruby Valley, Nev. 89833.

SHELDON NATIONAL ANTELOPE REFUGE and CHARLES SHELDON ANTELOPE RANGE • Totaling more than 554,000 acres, these refuges support desert bighorn, mule deer, pronghorn, Gambel's quail. Room 207, U.S. Post Office Bldg., Lakeview, Oreg. 97630.

STILLWATER NATIONAL WILDLIFE REFUGE** • 24,203 acres attracting whistling swans, geese, ducks, herons. Box 592, Fallon, Nev. 89406. Administered from Stillwater: Fallon National Wildlife Refuge, 17,900 acres; Anaho Island, 248 acres.

## NEW JERSEY

BRIGANTINE NATIONAL WILDLIFE REFUGE** • 18,100 acres for brant, ducks, shorebirds. Great Creek Road, Box 72, Oceanville, N.J. 08231.

GREAT SWAMP NATIONAL WILDLIFE REFUGE** • 6,000 acres for waterfowl, white-tailed deer, river otters. 614 Meyersville Rd., Gillette, N.J. 07933.

## NEW MEXICO

BITTER LAKE NATIONAL WILDLIFE REFUGE* • 24,100 acres for waterfowl, sandhill cranes, scaled quail, least terns. Box 7, Roswell, N.M. 88201.

BOSQUE DEL APACHE NATIONAL WILDLIFE REFUGE* • 57,200 acres used by waterfowl, sandhill cranes, scaled quail, least terns, mottled ducks. Box 278, San Antonio, N.M. 87832.

LAS VEGAS NATIONAL WILDLIFE REFUGE and MAXWELL NATIONAL WILDLIFE REFUGE** • 9,446 and 3,264 acres for waterfowl. Box 1070, Las Vegas, N.M. 87701.

SAN ANDRES NATIONAL WILDLIFE REFUGE** • 57,200 acres supporting bighorn sheep, mule deer, Gambel's and scaled quail. Box 756, Las Cruces, N.M. 88001.

## NEW YORK

IROQUOIS NATIONAL WILDLIFE REFUGE** • 10,799 acres attracting Canada geese, ducks, herons, muskrat. RFD 1, Bascom, N.Y. 14013.

MONTEZUMA NATIONAL WILDLIFE REFUGE** • 6,800

acres for geese, ducks, muskrat, deer. RFD 1, Box 232, Seneca Falls, N.Y. 13148.

## NORTH CAROLINA
CEDAR ISLAND NATIONAL WILDLIFE REFUGE** • 16,000 acres for waterfowl. Beaufort, N.C. 28516.

MATTAMUSKEET NATIONAL WILDLIFE REFUGE** • 50,177 acres for Canada geese, whistling swans, ducks, white-tailed deer. Box 606, New Holland, N.C. 27885. Administered from Mattamuskeet: Swanquarter National Wildlife Refuge, 15,500 acres.

PEA ISLAND NATIONAL WILDLIFE REFUGE* • 5,880 acres supporting greater snow and Canada geese, ducks, shorebirds, river otters. Box 606, Manteo, N.C. 27954.

PEE DEE NATIONAL WILDLIFE REFUGE** • 11,000 acres for ducks and Canada geese. Box 780, Wadesboro, N.C. 28170.

PUNGO NATIONAL WILDLIFE REFUGE** • 12,230 acres for waterfowl. Box 116, Plymouth, N.C. 27962.

## NORTH DAKOTA
ARROWWOOD NATIONAL WILDLIFE REFUGE* • 15,900 acres attracting whistling swans, geese, ducks. Rural Route 1, Edmunds, N.D. 58434.

AUDUBON NATIONAL WILDLIFE REFUGE** • 13,500 acres for mallards, teal, Canada geese. Route 1, Coleharbor, N.D. 58531.

DES LACS NATIONAL WILDLIFE REFUGE** • 18,900 acres for ducks, geese, grebes, sharp-tailed grouse. Box 578, Kenmare, N.D. 58746.

LONG LAKE NATIONAL WILDLIFE REFUGE • 22,300 acres for geese, ducks, Franklin's gulls, ring-necked pheasants, gray partridges. Moffit, N.D. 58560.

LOSTWOOD NATIONAL WILDLIFE REFUGE** • 22,750 acres supporting waterfowl, sharp-tailed grouse, sandhill cranes. Route 1, Lostwood, N.D. 58754.

J. CLARK SALYER NATIONAL WILDLIFE REFUGE** • 58,700 acres for geese, ducks, grebes, white pelicans, muskrat. Upham, N.D. 58789.

SLADE NATIONAL WILDLIFE REFUGE • 3,000 acres attracting waterfowl, sharp-tailed grouse, white-tailed deer. Dawson, N.D. 58428.

SULLYS HILL NATIONAL GAME PRESERVE* • 1,674 acres accommodating buffalo, deer, elk, geese. Fort Totten, N.D. 58335.

TEWAUKON NATIONAL WILDLIFE REFUGE • 7,800 acres supporting snow and blue geese, ducks, ring-necked pheasants. Route 1, Cayuga, N.D. 58013.

UPPER SOURIS NATIONAL WILDLIFE REFUGE* • 32,000 acres for geese, ducks, grouse, pheasants, sandhill cranes. Route 1, Foxholm, N.D. 58738.

## OHIO
OTTAWA NATIONAL WILDLIFE REFUGE** • 4,300 acres attracting black ducks, American widgeons, blue-winged teal, redheads, scaup, whistling swans. Route 3, Oak Harbor, Ohio 43449.

## OKLAHOMA
SALT PLAINS NATIONAL WILDLIFE REFUGE • 32,000 acres attracting geese, ducks, white pelicans, eagles, Franklin's gulls. Jet, Okla. 73749.

TISHOMINGO NATIONAL WILDLIFE REFUGE** • 16,500 acres for geese, ducks, herons, shorebirds. Box 248, Tishomingo, Okla. 73460.

WASHITA NATIONAL WILDLIFE REFUGE** • 8,100 acres for geese and ducks. Box 100, Butler, Okla. 73625.

WICHITA MOUNTAINS WILDLIFE REFUGE* • 59,020 acres supporting buffalo, elk, Texas longhorns, wild turkeys, Mississippi kites, bobwhites. Box 448, Cache, Okla. 73527.

## OREGON
HART MOUNTAIN NATIONAL ANTELOPE REFUGE • 240,700 acres for pronghorn, mule deer, sage grouse, California quail. Rooms 207, 208, and 304, U.S. Post Office Bldg., Lakeview, Ore. 97630.

MALHEUR NATIONAL WILDLIFE REFUGE** • 180,850 acres for whistling swans, ducks, sage grouse, California quail, white pelicans, glossy ibises, shorebirds. Box 113, Burns, Ore. 97720.

WILLIAM L. FINLEY NATIONAL WILDLIFE REFUGE** • 4,350 acres supporting Canada geese, ducks, band-tailed pigeons, pheasants, quail, mule deer. Box 208, Route 2, Corvallis, Ore. 97330.

## PENNSYLVANIA
ERIE NATIONAL WILDLIFE REFUGE** • 4,550 acres for geese, ducks, coots, grebes, herons, bitterns. RFD 3, Box 13, Guys Mills, Pa. 16327.

## SOUTH CAROLINA
CAPE ROMAIN NATIONAL WILDLIFE REFUGE* • 34,700 acres attracting geese, ducks, brown pelicans, shorebirds, rails, terns, loggerhead turtles, alligators. Box 228, McClellanville, S.C. 29458.

CAROLINA SANDHILLS NATIONAL WILDLIFE REFUGE* • 45,600 acres supporting bobwhites, wild turkeys, wood ducks. Box 130, Route 2, McBee, S.C. 29101.

SANTEE NATIONAL WILDLIFE REFUGE** • 73,300 acres for ducks, geese, herons. Box 186, Summerton, S.C. 29148.

## SOUTH DAKOTA
LACREEK NATIONAL WILDLIFE REFUGE** • 9,500 acres attracting geese, ducks, sharp-tailed grouse, shorebirds, white pelicans, trumpeter swans. South Rural Route, Martin, S.D. 57551.

Sand Lake National Wildlife Refuge* • 21,450 acres for blue and snow geese, ducks, ring-necked pheasants, Franklin's gulls. Rural Route, Columbia, S.D. 57433.

Waubay National Wildlife Refuge** • 4,650 acres attracting ducks, geese, ring-necked pheasants, Franklin's gulls, shorebirds, muskrat. Route 1, Waubay, S.D. 57273.

## TENNESSEE
Cross Creeks National Wildlife Refuge** • 9,000 acres supporting waterfowl, white-tailed deer, wild turkeys, bobwhites. Box 113-B, Route 1, Dover, Tenn. 37058.

Hatchie National Wildlife Refuge** • 11,000 acres for waterfowl. Box 187, Brownsville, Tenn. 38012.

Reelfoot National Wildlife Refuge** • 9,600 acres supporting ducks, geese, mourning doves, muskrat, mink. Box 295, Samburg, Tenn. 38254.

Tennessee National Wildlife Refuge* • 51,250 acres attracting ducks, geese, herons, white-tailed deer. Box 849, Paris, Tenn. 38242.

## TEXAS
Anahuac National Wildlife Refuge** • 9,800 acres for "lesser" Canada, snow, and blue geese, canvasbacks, red wolves. Box 278, Anahuac, Texas 77514. Administered from Anahuac: Brazoria National Wildlife Refuge, 6,367 acres.

Aransas National Wildlife Refuge* • 47,250 acres attracting whooping cranes, sandhill cranes, roseate spoonbills, egrets, shorebirds, hawks, collared peccaries. Box 68, Austwell, Texas 77950.

Buffalo Lake National Wildlife Refuge** • 7,700 acres for mallards, teal, widgeons, redheads, pintails. Box 229, Umbarger, Texas 79091.

Hagerman National Wildlife Refuge** • 11,400 acres supporting ducks and geese. Route 3, Box 123, Sherman, Texas 75090.

Laguna Atascosa National Wildlife Refuge** • 45,000 acres attracting geese, ducks, herons, ibises, shorebirds, gulls, terns, doves, cranes. Box 739, San Benito, Texas 78586.

Muleshoe National Wildlife Refuge** • 5,890 acres attractive to Canada geese, ducks, sandhill cranes, shorebirds, prairie dogs, scaled quail, burrowing owls. Box 549, Muleshoe, Texas 79347.

Santa Ana National Wildlife Refuge** • 2,000 acres for tree and mottled ducks, ibises, least grebes, red-billed pigeons, white-winged doves, chachalacas, green jays, Lichtenstein's orioles. Box 739, San Benito, Texas 78586.

## UTAH
Bear River Migratory Bird Refuge* • 65,000 acres attracting whistling swans, "western" Canada geese, ducks, grebes, white pelicans, shorebirds. Box 459, Brigham City, Utah 84302.

Fish Springs National Wildlife Refuge* • 18,000 acres supporting waterfowl, sandhill cranes, shorebirds, rails. Dugway, Utah 84022.

Ouray National Wildlife Refuge** • 10,350 acres for "western" Canada geese, ducks, wading birds, shorebirds. Box 191, Vernal, Utah 84078. Administered from Ouray: Brown's Park National Wildlife Refuge, 7,270 acres.

## VERMONT
Missisquoi National Wildlife Refuge** • 4,680 acres attracting Canada geese, black and wood ducks, woodcock, white-tailed deer, beaver. RFD 2, Swanton, Vt. 05488.

## VIRGINIA
Back Bay National Wildlife Refuge** • 9,000 acres supporting whistling swans, geese, ducks, shorebirds, muskrat. Box 6128, Virginia Beach, Va. 23456. Administered from Back Bay: Mackay Island National Wildlife Refuge, 6,200 acres.

Chincoteague National Wildlife Refuge* • 9,030 acres in Virginia and 417 acres in Maryland for greater snow geese, ducks, brant, shorebirds, gulls. P.O. Box 62, Chincoteague, Va. 23336.

Presquile National Wildlife Refuge • 1,329 acres for waterfowl. Box 658, Hopewell, Va. 23860.

## WASHINGTON
Columbia National Wildlife Refuge* • 28,400 acres for ducks and geese. Box 1465, Othello, Wash. 99344.

McNary National Wildlife Refuge** • 3,215 acres for waterfowl. Box 19, Burbank, Wash. 99323. Administered from McNary: Cold Springs National Wildlife Refuge, 3,117 acres; McKay Creek National Wildlife Refuge, 1,837 acres.

Ridgefield National Wildlife Refuge** • 6,100 acres supporting "dusky" Canada geese and other waterfowl. Box 476, Ridgefield, Wash. 98862.

Toppenish National Wildlife Refuge • 12,300 acres for ducks and geese. Box 271, Toppenish, Wash. 98948. Administered from Toppenish: Conboy Lake National Wildlife Refuge, 10,250 acres.

Turnbull National Wildlife Refuge* • 17,200 acres attracting trumpeter swans, Canada geese, ducks, ruffed grouse, California quail. Box 107, Route 3, Cheney, Wash. 99004.

Willapa National Wildlife Refuge* • 8,175 acres accommodating black brant, Canada geese, ducks, shorebirds, bald eagles, blue grouse, black bears.

Ilwaco, Wash. 98724. Administered from Willapa: Copalis National Wildlife Refuge, 5 acres; and Flattery Rocks and Quillayute Needles National Wildlife Refuges for cormorants, petrels, murres, auklets, oyster catchers, puffins, guillemots, shorebirds, gulls.

## WISCONSIN

HORICON NATIONAL WILDLIFE REFUGE** • 20,875 acres for Canada geese, ducks, whistling swans, muskrat, pheasants. Route 2, Mayville, Wis. 53050.

NECEDAH NATIONAL WILDLIFE REFUGE** • 39,600 acres for Canada geese, ducks, white-tailed deer, ruffed and sharp-tailed grouse, beaver, mink. Star Route, Necedah, Wis. 54646.

## WYOMING

HUTTON LAKE NATIONAL WILDLIFE REFUGE • 2,000 acres for ducks and geese. Box 759, Laramie, Wyo. 82070. Administered from Hutton Lake: Bamforth National Wildlife Refuge, 1,166 acres; Pathfinder National Wildlife Refuge, 16,800 acres.

SEEDSKADEE NATIONAL WILDLIFE REFUGE** • 18,000 acres for ducks and geese. Box 67, Green River, Wyo. 82935.

# *Illustration Credits*

An asterisk (*) following the photographer's name indicates that the photograph is used by courtesy of the Bureau of Sport Fisheries and Wildlife, United States Department of the Interior.

T—Top. B—Bottom. L—Left. R—Right.

Page 3. Jack Dermid. Page 9. Willis Peterson. 10. Clayton M. Hardy.* 14. T: James M. Thompson*; BL: Rex Gary Schmidt*; BR: Leonard Lee Rue III. 16. L: Ted Farrington, FPSA; R: Ernst Peterson.* 18. The Kansas State Historical Society. 19. Courtesy of Smithsonian Institution. 20–21. E. P. Haddon.* 22. Holland Mills. 24. National Audubon Society. 25. T: Don Bleitz, Bleitz Wildlife Foundation; B: Arthur A. Allen from National Audubon Society. 28. L: Rex Gary Schmidt*; R: John Winship.* 29. John Winship.* 31. T: Leonard Lee Rue III; B: John W. Corn. 34. Ray C. Erickson.* 35–36. David B. Marshall.* 38. Joseph Mazzoni.* 41. T: Ray C. Erickson*; B: David B. Marshall.* 42. L: Karl Maslowski*; R: Harry Engels. 44–45. Dr. I. N. Gabrielson.* 46. L: David B. Marshall*; R: Leonard Lee Rue III. 48. Leonard Lee Rue III. 49–51. E. P. Haddon.* 53. David B. Marshall.* 54. Eugene Kridler.* 55. T and BR: David B. Marshall*; BL: Eugene Kridler.* 56. T: David B. Marshall*; B: Eugene Kridler.* 59. T: Mal Lockwood; B: Tom McHugh from Photo Researchers, Inc. 60. Leonard Lee Rue III. 61. Willis Peterson. 63–64. Willard A. Troyer.* 65, 67. Leonard Lee Rue III. 68. Earl Fleming.* 71. Jerry L. Hout. 72. Alfred M. Bailey from National Audubon Society. 73. Robert Murphy. 75. Walter P. Taylor.* 77. William J. Bolte. 78. Earl Craven.* 79. Luther C. Goldman.* 80. Jack Dermid. 81. Charles L. Cadieux.* 84. T: Leonard Lee Rue III; B: Robert Murphy. 85. Luther C. Goldman.* 86. T: L. W. McDonald in *Frank Leslie's Illustrated Weekly;* B: E. P. Haddon.* 88. Charles D. Evans.* 92. James M. Thompson.* 93. L: Arthur W. Ambler from National Audubon Society; R: David McGlauchlin*; B: Leonard Lee Rue III. 95. Bureau of Sport Fisheries and Wildlife. 96. T: Thase Daniel; B: William Doerflinger. 97. L: Leonard Lee Rue III; R: W. F. Kubicheck.* 98. C. J. Henry.* 100. L: Herbert Troester*; R: Merrill C. Hammond.* 103. T: Jack Dermid; B: Andrew H. Dupre.* 104. Jack Dermid. 107. Robert Murphy. 108. E. P. Haddon.* 109. Leonard Lee Rue III. 110. Jack Dermid. 112. Frank R. Martin.* 114. Bureau of Sport Fisheries and Wildlife. 115. Leonard Lee Rue III. 116. Jack Dermid. 117. Leonard Lee Rue III. 118. L: Leonard Lee Rue III; R: Winston E. Banko.* 119. Allan D. Cruickshank from National Audubon Society.

albatross, 56; black-footed, 52, 53; Laysan, 52, 53, *55*

alligators, 102, 106, 108

American Fur Company, 51

American Museum, 18

anhinga, 102, 106, *109*

antelope, 18, 47; whitetail, 42. *See also* pronghorn

armadillo, 81, 87

Audubon, John James, 23

avocets, 23

badgers, 48, 80, 98

banding, 27, *28–29;* of woodcock, 117–18

bassaris, 80

bats, 42

bear: big brown (Kodiak), 21, 57, 58, 59, 62–66, *68;* black, 48, 58, 108, 113, *116;* grizzly, *48;* polar, 57; trapping of, 63, *64,* 66

beaver, 40, 42, 58, 67, 93, 98, 113; dam, *114;* extinction threatened, 17

Biological Survey, 19, 30, 94

bison, 15, *50–51. See also* buffalo

blackbird: red-winged, 11, 91; yellow-headed, 39, 91

Blitzen Valley, *41*

bobcats, 42, *81,* 113

boobies, 52, *54*

brant, black, 66

Bridger, Jim, 17

buffalo, 15, 25, 47–48, *49–50,* 82–83, 84; extinction threatened, 17–18, 48; hides, *18;* largest herd, 50; white (albino), *49,* 50

Bull's Island, *96*

bunting: snow, 66, 97; lark, 99

Bureau of Sport Fisheries and Wildlife, 14, 15, 19, 27, 89–90, 94

Cabeza de Vaca, 109

Canadian Wildlife Service, 90

caracara, 78

caribou, 57, 58; ground barren, *59*

Catlin, George, painting by, *19*

Cavelier, Charles, 94

chickadee, black-capped, 66

chukars, 49

Cincinnati Zoo, 23

coati, 80–81

collared peccary, *78,* 79

condor, California, 23

conservation, 14, 15, 16, 30, 61, 83; Wetlands Program and, 89–90

Cook, Captain, 61

cormorant, 103; double-crested, 94, *98*

Coronado, Francisco Vázquez de, 82

courtship dance, *36,* 39, 91, 99–100

coyote, 42, 58, 87, 97

cranes: *sandhill,* 23, *36,* 39, 40, *42,* 78, 94; whooping, 23, 40, 76–78, *79*

crossbill, white-winged, 66

curlews, 11, 23; bristle-thighed, 52; Eskimo, 23, *25;* long-billed, *16,* 103

Darling, Jay N., 16

deer: mule, *41,* 42, 47, 48; white-tailed, 47, 100

de Soto, Hernando, 109

dipper, 66

dowitcher, 103

ducks: black, 11, 114; canvasback, 26, 30, 92, 95–97, 100; eider, 111; gadwall, 39, 43; golden-eye, 61; mallard, 11, *14,* 26, 39, 43, 52, 91; pintail, 11, 43, 61, 92; redhead, 26, 39, 43, *93,* 100; ring-necked, *96,* 114; ruddy, 43, 91; shoveler, 92; teal, blue-winged, 91–92, *93,* cinnamon, 39, 43, green-winged, 61, 92, Laysan, 52; wood, 103, 114

dunlins, 103

eagles: bald, 11, 61, *63,* 66, 92, 114; golden, 39, 40, *42,* 92, 98; extinction threatened, 19–20; Olympic, 67

egrets, *35,* 78, 102, 103

elk, *20–21,* 25, 37, 47, 48, 82, 87; extinction threatened, 19–20; Olympic, 67

falcon, peregrine, 103

ferret, black-footed, 25

finch, Laysan, *55*

Fish and Wildlife Service, 27

fishers, 113–14, *118*

flyways, 30; Atlantic Flyway, 32, 101, 106, 111; Central Flyway, 33, 75, 99; maps of, *32–33;* Mississippi Flyway, 32, 44, 91, 101; Pacific Flyway, 33, 37, 43, 46, 75

fox: Arctic, *60;* gray, 80, 87; red, 87, 98, 113

frigate bird, 52, 54, *55*

geese: blue, 26, 92; cackling, 43; Canada, *10,* 11, *14,* 15, 26, 29, 39, *43–46,* 66, 92, 94, 102, *112,* subspecies of, 43–44; emperor,

66; snow, 11, 26, 43, 66, 92, 101; white-fronted, 43, 66

godwits, 23; marbled, 103

gopher, Plains pocket, 80

goshawks, 61

grebe: eared, 94, *97;* Holboell's, 94, *97;* horned, 94, 103; pied-billed, 94; western, *9,* 39, 94

grosbeak: evening, 117; pine, 66, 117

grouse: blue, 48–49; ruffed, 28, 97, 117; sage, 37; sharp-tailed, 37, 97, 98, 99; spruce, 61, 117

gulls, 103; Franklin's, 91, 94

hawks, 11; ferruginous, *34;* marsh, 11, *14;* red-shouldered, 106; red-tailed, 11; white-tailed, 78

Henry, Alexander, 94

herons, 11, 78, 102, 103, 106; black-crowned, 94; blue, 11, 94

Hoover, Herbert, 42

ibis: glossy, 102; white, 78, 106; wood, 103, 106

J. Clark Salyer, 16

jack rabbit, *75;* blacktail, 42, 80, 87; cottontail, 80; whitetail, 48

jay, Canada, 117

juncos, 29

kingfishers, 66, 106

kite, Everglade, 23, *119*

knots, 103

La Vérendrye, Pierre Gaultier de Varennes de, 50, 94

Laysan Island, *53*

Lewis and Clark, 51

Lincoln, Frederick C., 30

longhorn cattle, 82, 83–87, *86*

longspur, Lapland, 117

loons, 61, 66, 114

lynx, 58

MacKay, Douglas, 61

marmot, hoary, 58, 60, *61*

marten, 67

mating dance. *See* courtship dance

migration of birds, 26, 27–33, 43; hibernation and, 27, 28

migration habits: of Arctic tern, 28; of barn swallow, 28; of blackpoll warbler, 28; of blue-winged teal, 91–92; of Canada geese, 29, 46; of cliff swallow, 28; of wheatears, 28

Migratory Bird Populations Station, 30

miller bird, Nihoa, *56*
mink, 40, 48, 58, 67, 93, 98, 113
moose, 57, 58, 61, 93, 113, *114;* calf, *92;* Kenai, 21
mountain goats, 58, 60
musk oxen, 57, 69, 70, *71–74*
muskrat, 39, 40, 42, 48, 67, 93, 98, 113

Narváez, Pánfilo de, 109
National Parks, 15, 19, 48
National Wilderness Preservation System, 61
National Wildlife Refuge System: division of, 14; information on, obtaining, 15; map of, 12–13; number of refuges in, 14. *See also* refuges
National Wildlife Refuges: Agassiz, 91–93, map of, 92; Alaskan, 21, 57–74, *73*, map of, 73; Aleutian Islands, 21; Aransas, 23, 76–81, map of, 78; Bear River, 30; Bombay Hook, 11, map of, 15; Brigantine, 111; Cape Romain, 102–5, map of, 105; Charles M. Russell, 37; Charles Sheldon Antelope, 19; Clear Lake, 43; Colusa, 37; Desert National, 37, *75;* Fish Springs, 75; Great Swamp, 111; Hart Mountain, 19; Hawaiian Islands, 52–56, *53*, map of, 54; Hazy Island, 57; Iroquois, 111, *112;* J. Clark Salyer, 94–98, map of, 95; Kenai National Moose, 58–61, map of, 60; Klamath Basin, 30, 37, 43–46, map of, 44; Klamath Forest, 43; Kodiak, 62–67, *68*, map of, 63; Lostwood, 99–100, map of, 99; Lower Klamath, 43; Loxahatchee, 101; Malheur, 16, 26, 30, *34, 36*, 39–42, map of, 40; Mattamuskeet, 101; Monomoy, 111; Moosehorn, 113–18, *114*, map of, 114; National Bison, 18, 19, *38*, 47–51, map of, 48; National Elk, 20, 75; National Key Deer, 101; Nunivak, 69–74, map of, 70; Okefenokee, 106–10, *107*, map of, 108; Pea Island, 101; Pelican Island, 25; Sacramento, 37, *46;* Sanibel, 101; Seney, 44; Sheldon Antelope, 19; Sutter, 37; Tule Lake, 30, 43; Upper Klamath, 43; Upper Mississippi, 30; Wheeler, 101; White River, 101; Wichita Mountains, 18, 82–87, *84*, map of, 83
New York Zoo, 18, 82
Nihoa Island, *53*
noddies, 53
nutcracker, Clark's, 48

ocelot, 81
opossums, *3, 80*
osprey, 106
otters, 40, 42, 93, 106, 113; sea, 67, extinction threatened, 20–21
owl: barred, 108; boreal, 117; burrowing, *84;* great gray, 92; horned, 39, 61; snowy, 92, 98, 117
oyster catchers, 103

parakeet, Carolina, 23
partridge, gray, 49, 98, 99
passenger pigeon, 23, *24*
pauraque, 78
pelicans, 94; brown, *22*, 25, 103; white, 39, *44–45*
petrels, 52, 54, 56
phalarope: red, 52; Wilson's, 95
pheasant, ring-necked, 49, 98
Pinchot, Gifford, 16
pipits, Sprague's, 99
plovers, 23, 103; black-bellied, 52; golden, 30, *31,* 52; piping, 99
poorwill, 28
porcupine, 42, 98, 113, 114, *118*
Pothole Country, 89
potholes, *88*, 89, 90, 95, 99, *100*
prairie chicken, Attwater's, 81
prairie dogs, 25, *85;* black-tailed, 87
pronghorn, 15, *19*, 37, 42, 47, 100; extinction threatened, 18–19
ptarmigan, 61, 66
puffin, horned, *65*
puma, Florida, 108
pyrrhuloxia, 78

raccoons, 80, 98
rails, 23, 56; clapper, 103; flightless, 52
rats: kangaroo, 42; bushy-tailed wood, 42
raven, 66, 117
redpoll, common, 97
redstarts, 30
refuges: conservation and, 14, 15, 25; early purpose of, 15, 21; first, 25; first, for big-game animals, 18; first, for ducks and geese, 25–26; information on, obtaining, 15; migration and, 26, 30; visiting, 15–16, 30. *See also* National Wildlife Refuge System; National Wildlife Refuges
reindeer, 57, 67, *72*
road runner, 78
Roosevelt, Franklin, 42, 82
Roosevelt, Theodore, 16, 18, 42, 47, 52

salmon, 62–63
sanderlings, *103*

scaup, 92
scoters, 111
seals: harbor, 113; Hawaiian monk, 52, *56*
Seton, Ernest Thompson, 18
shearwaters, 52, 54
sheep: bighorn, 37, *38*, 42, 47, 48; Dall's, 58, 59
shrike, northern, 97
siskin, pine, 66
skimmer, black, 103
skunk, 98; spotted, 42; striped, 48, 80
Smith, John, 118
snipe, 23
snowshoe hare, 48, *67*, 113
Souris River, *95*
sparrows, 61; Baird's, 99; fox, 66; Ipswich, 30; LeConte's, 95; song, 66; tree, 117
spoonbill, roseate, *77*, 78
squirrel, flying, *116–17*
stilt, black-necked, *31*, 78
swallows, 28, 61
swans: trumpeter, 15, 23, 39, 58; whistling, 92, 101

tanager, western, 48
tattler, wandering, 52
tern: Arctic, 28; black, 39, 91; fairy, 53, *54–55*; Forster's, 39; grayback, 53; royal, *104;* sooty, 53
toad, Eastern spadefoot, *110*
tropic bird, 52, *53–54*
turkeys, 37; water, 102; wild, 37, 79, 87, 103
turnstones, 103; ruddy, 52
turtle: green sea, 52; loggerhead, *103*

vireos, 117

walrus, 57
wapiti, 19
warblers, 61, 117; blackpoll, 28; Kirtland's, 23
water moccasin, cottonmouth, *110*
waxwing, Bohemian, 97–98
weasels, 98, *100*, 113
Wetlands Program, 26, 30, 89–90, 97
wheatears, 28
whimbrel, Bohemian, 97–98
white whales, 74
wild boar, 79–80
willets, 103
wolverine, 58, *59*
wolves, 58; buffalo, 48; red, 80, 87, 108; timber, *93*
woodcock, 117–18
woodpecker: ivory-billed, 23, *25*, 106; Lewis', 48; pileated, 102

yellowlegs, 23, 103

**333.7**
**M**
**MURPHY, ROBERT**
  A heritage restored

| DATE DUE | | | |
|---|---|---|---|
|  |  |  |  |
|  |  |  |  |
|  |  |  |  |
|  |  |  |  |
|  |  |  |  |
|  |  |  |  |
|  |  |  |  |
|  |  |  |  |
|  |  |  |  |
|  |  |  |  |
|  |  |  | ALESCO |